TEACHER EDITION • Chapter 3

Basic Facts and Relationships

Houghton Mifflin Harcourt

Copyright © 2015 by Houghton Mifflin Harcourt Publishing Company

Printed in the U.S.A.

ISBN 978-0-544-29578-0

10 11 12 13 14 15 16 2266   23 22 21 20 19 18 17
4500656625   DEFG

Critical Area # Addition and Subtraction

Common Core (CRITICAL AREA) Building fluency with addition and subtraction

Lessons ## Grade 2 Common Core State Standards

Domain: Operations and Algebraic Thinking   2.OA

		Cluster A: 2.OA.A.1	Represent and solve problems involving addition and subtraction.
3.8–3.9	■		Use addition and subtraction within 100 to solve one- and two-step word problems involving situations of adding to, taking from, putting together, taking apart, and comparing, with unknowns in all positions, e.g., by using drawings and equations with a symbol for the unknown number to represent the problem.
3.1–3.7	■	Cluster B: 2.OA.B.2	Add and subtract within 20. Fluently add and subtract within 20 using mental strategies. By end of Grade 2, know from memory all sums of two one-digit numbers.
3.10–3.11	☐	Cluster C: 2.OA.C.4	Work with equal groups of objects to gain foundations for multiplication. Use addition to find the total number of objects arranged in rectangular arrays with up to 5 rows and up to 5 columns; write an equation to express the total as a sum of equal addends.

Key: Major Clusters: ■   Supporting Clusters: ☐   Additional Clusters: ○

Table of Contents

Chapter 3 Basic Facts and Relationships

Domain:
Operations and Algebraic Thinking   2.OA

Connecting Domains and Clusters:
* This chapter also includes the following standards: 2.NBT.B.5, 2.MD.B.6

MATHEMATICAL PRACTICES

MP1 Make sense of problems and persevere in solving them.

MP2 Reason abstractly and quantitatively.

MP3 Construct viable arguments and critique the reasoning of others.

MP4 Model with mathematics.

MP5 Use appropriate tools strategically.

MP6 Attend to precision.

MP7 Look for and make use of structure.

MP8 Look for and express regularity in repeated reasoning.

Addition and Subtraction

 Common Core CRITICAL AREA **Building fluency with addition and subtraction**

Common Core PROFESSIONAL DEVELOPMENT

See Teaching for Depth, pp. 159E, 233E, 313E, 387E.

See Mathematical Practices in every lesson.

Digital Resources

FOR LEARNING...

 ## Interactive Student Edition

- Immerses students in an interactive, multi-sensory math environment
- Enhances learning with scaffolded, interactive instruction and just-in-time feedback
- Provides audio reinforcement for each lesson
- Makes learning a two-way experience, using a variety of interactive tools

FOR ASSESSMENT AND INTERVENTION...

 ## Personal Math Trainer

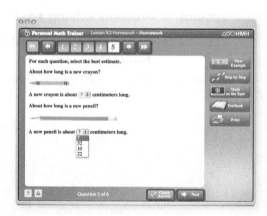

- Creates a personalized learning path for each student
- Provides opportunities for practice, homework, and assessment
- Includes worked-out examples and helpful video support
- Offers targeted intervention and extra support to build proficiency and understanding

FOR DAILY MATH TUTORING...

 ## Math on the Spot Videos

- Models good problem-solving thinking in every lesson
- Engages students through interesting animations and fun characters
- Builds student problem-solving proficiency and confidence
- Builds the skills needed for success on the Common Core Assessments

FOR SIMPLICITY...

 HMH Player App

It's For Students ...

- Content is available online, offline, and on-the-go!
- Students are engaged in class, at home, and anywhere in between for uninterrupted instruction
- Raise a Hand for instant student-teacher-student communication

... And For Teachers!

- Teachers can monitor student progress in real time
- Lesson customization features allow teachers to deliver personalized learning
- Plan your lessons, make assignments, and view results from the convenience of your classroom, at home, or on-the-go
- Supports blended learning through anywhere digital instruction

FOR TEACHING...

 **Digital Management System**

- Manage online all program content and components
- Search for and select resources based on Common Core State Standards
- Identify resources based on student ability and needs
- View and assign student lessons, practice, assessments, and more

Professional Development Videos

- Learn more about the Common Core and Common Core content
- See first-hand the integration of the Mathematical Practices
- Watch students engaged in a productive struggle

Critical Area Pacing Chart

Introduction	Chapters	Assessment	Total
Vocabulary Reader		Performance Assessment	
1 day	71 days	1 day	73 days

1 READ

All About Animals

Objective Use literature to review addition concepts.

Genre Nonfiction

Domains: Operations and Algebraic Thinking
Number and Operations in Base Ten

▶ **Preparing to Read** Refer children to the story cover and read the title. Have children flip through the pages and identify the animals on each page.

Explain that they will read the story together and solve math problems. Then they will read the story again and learn some fun animal facts. They will use the facts to help them answer science questions about how animals care for their young.

▶ **Story Vocabulary** giraffe, ostrich, kangaroo, mobs, wild boars, snout, sounders, moose, antlers, gallop

▶ **Reading the Math Story**
Pages 151–154

Each story passage describes two groups. The groups must be added together to answer the question on each page.

- **What number sentence can you write to find the number of giraffes in all? Explain.**
  5 + 5 = 10; there are two groups and there are five in each group, so you add to find the sum.

- **What number sentence can you write to find the total number of eggs in the nest?**
  6 + 5 = 11 or 5 + 6 = 11

- **What number sentence can you write to find the total number of kangaroos in the mob?** 8 + 4 = 12 or 4 + 8 = 12

Vocabulary Reader · Critical Area · Addition and Subtraction

All About Animals
by John Hudson

Common Core · Building fluency with addition and subtraction

151

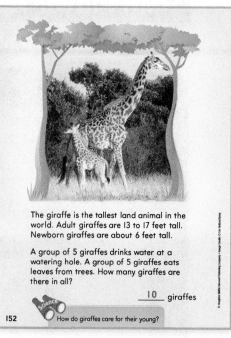

The giraffe is the tallest land animal in the world. Adult giraffes are 13 to 17 feet tall. Newborn giraffes are about 6 feet tall.

A group of 5 giraffes drinks water at a watering hole. A group of 5 giraffes eats leaves from trees. How many giraffes are there in all?

_10_ giraffes

152   How do giraffes care for their young?

The ostrich is the largest bird in the world. Ostriches cannot fly, but they can run fast. Ostrich eggs weigh about 3 pounds each! Several ostriches will lay eggs in a shared nest.

There are 6 eggs in a nest. Then 5 more eggs are put in that nest. How many eggs are in the nest now?

_11_ eggs

How do ostriches care for their young?   153

Kangaroos can move quickly by jumping with their two back legs. When they are moving slowly, they use all four legs.

Western gray kangaroos live in groups called mobs. There are 8 kangaroos in a mob. 4 more kangaroos join the mob. How many kangaroos are in the mob in all?

_12_ kangaroos

154   How do kangaroos care for their young?

Wild boars like to eat roots. They use their tough snouts to dig. Wild boars can be up to 6 feet long.

Wild boars live in groups called sounders. There is one sounder of 14 boars. If 7 of the boars are eating, how many boars are not eating?

___7___ boars

How do wild boars care for their young? **155**

Moose are the largest kind of deer. Male moose have antlers that may be 5 to 6 feet wide. Moose can trot and gallop. They are also good swimmers!

A ranger saw 7 moose in the morning and 6 moose in the afternoon. How many moose did the ranger see that day?

__13__ moose

156 How do moose care for their young?

Name _____

Write About the Story

Choose one kind of animal. Draw and write your own story about that kind of animal. Use addition in your story.

Vocabulary Review
add   in all

giraffe   ostrich   kangaroo   Check children's work.

WRITE › Math

157

How many eggs are there?

Draw more ostrich eggs in each nest. Write an addition sentence below each nest to show how many eggs are in each nest now. Check children's work.

MATH BOARD Choose a different animal from the story. Write another story that uses addition.

158

Pages 155–156

Children should understand the story progression. Have children share how they solved each problem.

- **How did you find the number of boars not eating?** Possible answer: I knew that 7 boars were eating and that there were 14 boars in all, so I thought 7 plus how many more is 14. I know that $7 + 7 = 14$.

- **What addition strategy could you use to find the total number of moose?** Possible answer: I need to add 7 and 6 so I could double 6 and then add 1.

2 RESPOND

Write About the Story

Page 157

WRITE › Math Ask children to choose one animal from the story. Have them draw a picture and write a story about their animal. Encourage children to use addition and the review vocabulary in their stories. Ask volunteers to share their stories with the class.

▶ **Math Vocabulary** add, in all

Do the Math

- **How many eggs are there?**

Page 158

In this activity, children draw additional eggs in each ostrich nest and write addition sentences to match. Then challenge children to write another addition story about a different animal.

Real World Connections to Science

Read the story again as children follow along. Then read aloud the fun facts about animals listed below. Have children look at the story pictures and discuss the Science question on each page.

Giraffe Facts:

- Newborn giraffes are hidden for their first month of life to protect them from other animals.
- After about two months, baby calves are left in "nursery groups" while the mothers feed.

Ostrich Facts:

- Ostriches use their bodies to protect their young. For example, adult ostriches cover chicks with their wings. This protects the chicks from the sun, rain, and dangerous animals.
- Ostriches use their long necks and good eyesight to watch for danger.

Kangaroo Facts:

- Kangaroos keep their young in a special place. This place is a mother's front pouch.
- Baby kangaroos are called joeys. They stay inside their mothers' pouches for 7–10 months.
- Joeys grow inside the pouch until they are ready to stand up on their own.

Moose Facts:

- Moose calves are able to follow their mother hours after being born.
- The mother moose stays with her calf for about one year.
- The mother helps her calf by feeding it the healthiest plants she can find.

Wild Boar Facts:

- Mother wild boars are called sows.
- Sows get together in groups to protect their piglets from danger.
- The sows form a circle and place their piglets in the center.

Online Projects p. B3

© Houghton Mifflin Harcourt Publishing Company

Choose numbers from the box to complete each story. Use each number only once.

15	6
	9	
8	5
	13	

Order of answers may vary.

___9___ monkeys in a troop.

___6___ more come to play.

Now ___15___ monkeys are in the troop.

___5___ leopards in a leap.

___8___ join them.

Now ___13___ leopards are in the leap.

B3

Page 4

A Bunch of Animals

My Pictures

A Math Storybook

by _____

CRITICAL AREA Building fluency with addition and subtraction

Online Projects p. B4

Have you ever seen a bunch of ducks or geese? Each bunch of animals has a special name.

Do you know any of these?

A gaggle of geese
A brace of ducks
A troop of monkeys
A leap of leopards
A gang of elks
A band of gorillas
A pride of lions

Page 2

© Houghton Mifflin Harcourt Publishing Company

Read each story. Write the name of the animals. Then answer the question.

5 ___lions___ in the pride.
9 more join the group.
How many in the pride now?
___14 lions___

8 ___geese___ in a gaggle.
7 more come along.
How many in the gaggle now?
___15 geese___

Page 3

B4

My Math Project Storybook

A Bunch of Animals

Objective Review addition facts.

Materials Online Projects pp. B3–B4, crayons

Print and copy the pages from the Online Projects and help children fold them to make their own storybooks. Explain that they will work together to complete stories about groups of animals.

Remind children that a group of kangaroos is called a mob, and a group of boars is called a sounder. Page 2 of the storybook lists special names for some other groups of animals. Have children follow along as you read the list.

On page 3, children fill in the missing names of the animals and answer story questions. Have them refer back to page 2 for help with animal group names.

On page 4, children write numbers to complete each animal story. Tell them to choose numbers from the box and not to repeat any numbers.

After children have completed the pages, have them share their work with the class, and then take their storybooks home to share with family members.

Performance Assessment You may suggest that children place completed projects in their portfolios.

Chapter At A Glance

Domain: Operations and Algebraic Thinking

Chapter Essential Question How can you use patterns and strategies to find sums and differences for basic facts?

Use the *GO Math! Planning Guide* for correlations, mathematical practices information, and more.

Lesson At A Glance

	1 Day **LESSON 3.1** 2.OA.B.2	**2 Days** **LESSON 3.2** 2.OA.B.2	**1 Day** **LESSON 3.3** 2.OA.B.2
	Use Doubles Facts.........163A	**Practice Addition Facts.........169A**	**Algebra • Make a Ten to Add.........175A**
Essential Question	How can you use doubles facts to find sums for near doubles facts?	What are some ways to remember sums?	How is the make a ten strategy used to find sums?
Objective	Use doubles facts as a strategy for finding sums for near doubles facts.	Recall sums for basic facts using properties and strategies.	Recall sums for addition facts using the make a ten strategy.
Vocabulary	**sums, doubles**	**addends, count on, number sentence**	
ELL Strategy	**ELL** Strategy • Illustrate Understanding	**ELL** Strategy • Model Concepts	**ELL** Strategy • Model Concepts

GO DIGITAL

Go online to access all your chapter resources

www.thinkcentral.com

3.1 eStudent Edition	3.2 eStudent Edition	3.3 eStudent Edition
3.1 eTeacher Edition	3.2 eTeacher Edition	3.3 eTeacher Edition
Personal Math Trainer	Personal Math Trainer	Personal Math Trainer
Math on the Spot Video	Math on the Spot Video	Math on the Spot Video
Animated Math Models	Animated Math Models	Animated Math Models
iT iTools	*iT* iTools	*iT* iTools
HMH Mega Math	HMH Mega Math	HMH Mega Math

Print Resources

3.1 Student Edition	3.2 Student Edition	3.3 Student Edition
3.1 Practice and Homework (in the *Student Edition*)	3.2 Practice and Homework (in the *Student Edition*)	3.3 Practice and Homework (in the *Student Edition*)
3.1 Reteach (in the *Chapter Resources*)	3.2 Reteach (in the *Chapter Resources*)	3.3 Reteach (in the *Chapter Resources*)
3.1 Enrich (in the *Chapter Resources*)	3.2 Enrich (in the *Chapter Resources*)	3.3 Enrich (in the *Chapter Resources*)
Grab-and-Go™ Centers Kit	Grab-and-Go™ Centers Kit	Grab-and-Go™ Centers Kit

RtI

Response to Intervention

Before the Chapter	During the Lesson	After the Chapter
✓ Show What You Know	✓ Share and Show	✓ Chapter Review/Test
• Prerequisite Skills Activities • Personal Math Trainer	• RtI Tier 1 Lesson (online) • Mid-Chapter Checkpoint • Personal Math Trainer	• RtI Tier 1 Lesson (online) • Personal Math Trainer

2 Days
LESSON 3.4   2.OA.B.2

Algebra • Add 3 Addends 181A

How do you add three numbers?

Find sums of three addends by applying the Commutative and Associative Properties of Addition.

sum, addends

ELL Strategy • Model Concepts

---

2 Days
LESSON 3.5   2.OA.B.2

Algebra • Relate Addition and Subtraction 187A

How are addition and subtraction related?

Use the inverse relationship of addition and subtraction to recall basic facts.

differences, related facts

ELL Strategy • Identify Relationships

---

2 Days
LESSON 3.6   2.OA.B.2

Practice Subtraction Facts 193A

What are some ways to remember differences?

Recall differences for basic facts using mental strategies.

count back

ELL Strategy • Develop Meanings

3.4 *e*Student Edition
3.4 *e*Teacher Edition
- Personal Math Trainer
- Math on the Spot Video
- Animated Math Models
- *i*T *i*Tools
- HMH Mega Math

3.5 *e*Student Edition
3.5 *e*Teacher Edition
- Personal Math Trainer
- Math on the Spot Video
- Animated Math Models
- *i*T *i*Tools
- HMH Mega Math

3.6 *e*Student Edition
3.6 *e*Teacher Edition
- Personal Math Trainer
- Math on the Spot Video
- Animated Math Models
- *i*T *i*Tools
- HMH Mega Math

3.4 Student Edition
3.4 Practice and Homework
(in the *Student Edition*)
3.4 Reteach (in the *Chapter Resources*)
3.4 Enrich (in the *Chapter Resources*)
Grab-and-Go™ Centers Kit

3.5 Student Edition
3.5 Practice and Homework
(in the *Student Edition*)
3.5 Reteach (in the *Chapter Resources*)
3.5 Enrich (in the *Chapter Resources*)
Grab-and-Go™ Centers Kit

3.6 Student Edition
3.6 Practice and Homework
(in the *Student Edition*)
3.6 Reteach (in the *Chapter Resources*)
3.6 Enrich (in the *Chapter Resources*)
Grab-and-Go™ Centers Kit

GO DIGITAL

Resources   www.thinkcentral.com

- **SE** Interactive Student Edition
- Personal Math Trainer
- Math on the Spot Video
- Animated Math Models
- ✓ Assessment
- HMH Mega Math
- *i*T *i*Tools
- ABC Multimedia *e*Glossary
- Professional Development Videos

Basic Facts and Relationships   **159B**

Chapter At A Glance

Domain: Operations and Algebraic Thinking

	2 Days **LESSON 3.7** 2.OA.B.2	**2 Days** **LESSON 3.8** 2.OA.A.1	**2 Days** **LESSON 3.9** 2.OA.A.1
Lesson At A Glance	**Use Ten to Subtract** 199A	**Algebra • Use Drawings to Represent Problems** 205A	**Algebra • Use Equations to Represent Problems** 211A
Essential Question	How does getting to 10 in subtraction help when finding differences?	How are bar models used to show addition and subtraction problems?	How are number sentences used to show addition and subtraction situations?
Objective	Find differences on a number line to develop the mental strategy of decomposing to simplify facts.	Use bar models to represent a variety of addition and subtraction situations.	Write equations to represent and solve a variety of addition and subtraction situations.
Vocabulary	**difference**	**bar model**	**number sentence**
ELL Strategy	**ELL Strategy** • Model Concepts	**ELL Strategy** • Understand Context	**ELL Strategy** • Model Concepts

GO DIGITAL

Go online to access all your chapter resources

www.thinkcentral.com

3.7 *eStudent Edition* 3.7 *eTeacher Edition* Personal Math Trainer Math on the Spot Video *iT* *iTools*	3.8 *eStudent Edition* 3.8 *eTeacher Edition* Personal Math Trainer Math on the Spot Video Animated Math Models *iT* *iTools*	3.9 *eStudent Edition* 3.9 *eTeacher Edition* Personal Math Trainer Math on the Spot Video Animated Math Models *iT* *iTools* HMH Mega Math

Print Resources

3.7 Student Edition 3.7 Practice and Homework (in the *Student Edition*) 3.7 Reteach (in the *Chapter Resources*) 3.7 Enrich (in the *Chapter Resources*) Grab-and-Go™ Centers Kit	3.8 Student Edition 3.8 Practice and Homework (in the *Student Edition*) 3.8 Reteach (in the *Chapter Resources*) 3.8 Enrich (in the *Chapter Resources*) Grab-and-Go™ Centers Kit	3.9 Student Edition 3.9 Practice and Homework (in the *Student Edition*) 3.9 Reteach (in the *Chapter Resources*) 3.9 Enrich (in the *Chapter Resources*) Grab-and-Go™ Centers Kit

Assessment

Diagnostic	Formative	Summative

• Show What You Know
• Diagnostic Interview Task
• Digital Personal Math Trainer
	• Lesson Quick Check
	• Mid-Chapter Checkpoint
	• Digital Personal Math Trainer
	  - Assessment Animation
	  - Assessment Video
		• Chapter Review/Test
		• Chapter Test
		• Performance Assessment Task
		• Digital Personal Math Trainer

I Day
LESSON 3.10 ☐ 2.OA.C.4

Problem Solving • Equal Groups 217A

How can acting it out help when solving a problem about equal groups?

Solve problems involving equal groups by using the strategy *act it out.*

ELL Strategy • Illustrate Understanding

3.10 *e*Student Edition

3.10 *e*Teacher Edition

🐭 **Personal Math Trainer**

📺 **Math on the Spot Video**

〰️ **HMH Mega Math**

3.10 Student Edition

3.10 Practice and Homework (in the *Student Edition*)

3.10 Reteach (in the *Chapter Resources*)

3.10 Enrich (in the *Chapter Resources*)

Grab-and-Go™ Centers Kit

I Day
LESSON 3.11 ☐ 2.OA.C.4

Algebra • Repeated Addition 223A

How can you write an addition sentence for problems with equal groups?

Write equations using repeated addition to find the total number of objects in arrays.

row, addition sentence

ELL Strategy • Model Language

3.11 *e*Student Edition

3.11 *e*Teacher Edition

🐭 **Personal Math Trainer**

📺 **Math on the Spot Video**

✓ **Chapter 3 Test**

〰️ **HMH Mega Math**

3.11 Student Edition

3.11 Practice and Homework (in the *Student Edition*)

3.11 Reteach (in the *Chapter Resources*)

3.11 Enrich (in the *Chapter Resources*)

Grab-and-Go™ Centers Kit

Teacher Notes

Teaching for Depth

Matt Larson
Curriculum Specialist for Mathematics
Lincoln Public Schools
Lincoln, Nebraska

Thinking Strategies for Addition

Fluency is based on instructional strategies that are developed conceptually, rather than based on rote practice and memorization (Fuson, 2003; NRC, 2001).

Thinking strategies for addition facts are directly related to one or more number relationships and include the following (Van de Walle, 2004):

+	0	1	2	3	4	5	6	7	8	9
0	0	1	2	3	4	5	6	7	8	9
1	1	2	3	4	5	6	7	8	9	10
2	2	3	4	5	6	7	8	9	10	11
3	3	4	5	6	7	8	9	10	11	12
4	4	5	6	7	8	9	10	11	12	13
5	5	6	7	8	9	10	11	12	13	14
6	6	7	8	9	10	11	12	13	14	15
7	7	8	9	10	11	12	13	14	15	16
8	8	9	10	11	12	13	14	15	16	17
9	9	10	11	12	13	14	15	16	17	18

- Facts that have one addend of 1 or 2 (36 facts).

- Facts that have zero as one of the addends (19 facts).

- Doubles facts (10 facts).

- Make a ten by giving some quantity from one addend to the other addend (Fuson, 2003). This can be enhanced through the ten frame.

From the Research

"Examining the relationships between addition and subtraction and seeing subtraction as involving a known and unknown addend are examples of adaptive reasoning. By providing experiences for young students to develop adaptive reasoning in addition and subtraction situations, teachers are also anticipating algebra as students begin to appreciate the inverse relationships between the two operations." (NRC, 2001, p. 191)

Thinking Strategies for Subtraction

Teaching for understanding is enhanced when instruction focuses on tasks and strategies that help students develop relationships within addition and subtraction combinations (NCTM, 2000).

Learning to think of subtraction as addition can make subtraction as easy as, or easier than, addition (Fuson, 2003).

- Rather than thinking of 14 – 8, children can be encouraged to focus on 8 and what other number make 14.

- This strategy focuses on part-part-whole relations, which have been shown to be particularly effective at supporting students' development of efficient thinking subtraction strategies (NRC, 2001).

- Emphasizing part-part-whole relations helps students develop an understanding of related facts and inverse operations, and their ability to recognize when to add and when to subtract (NRC, 2001).

Common Core | Mathematical Practices

Teachers who want to develop deep understanding in their students encourage them to share the strategies they use for addition and subtraction combinations during class discussions. Students develop and refine strategies during math talk as they hear other students' descriptions of their thinking (NCTM, 2000). Discussing their explanations gives children an opportunity to **attend to precision**.

Professional Development Videos:
The Meaning of Addition and Subtraction, Grades K–2, Segments 2, 4, 5

Daily Classroom Management

Differentiated Instruction

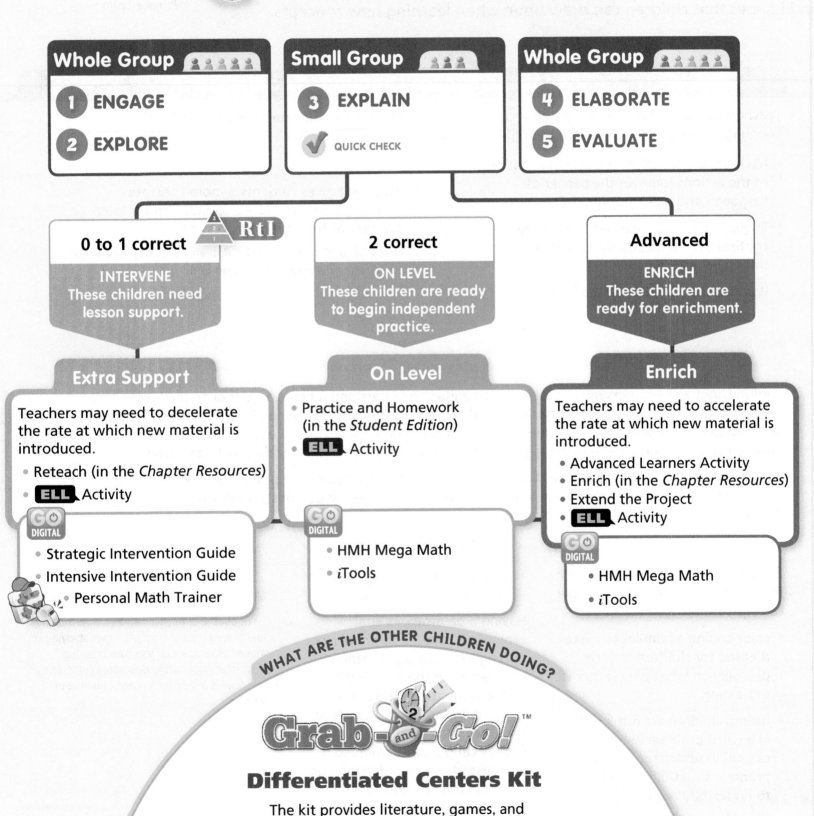

Whole Group	Small Group	Whole Group
1 ENGAGE	**3** EXPLAIN	**4** ELABORATE
2 EXPLORE	✓ QUICK CHECK	**5** EVALUATE

RtI

0 to 1 correct

INTERVENE
These children need lesson support.

2 correct

ON LEVEL
These children are ready to begin independent practice.

Advanced

ENRICH
These children are ready for enrichment.

Extra Support

Teachers may need to decelerate the rate at which new material is introduced.
- Reteach (in the *Chapter Resources*)
- **ELL** Activity

GO DIGITAL
- Strategic Intervention Guide
- Intensive Intervention Guide
- Personal Math Trainer

On Level

- Practice and Homework (in the *Student Edition*)
- **ELL** Activity

GO DIGITAL
- HMH Mega Math
- *i*Tools

Enrich

Teachers may need to accelerate the rate at which new material is introduced.
- Advanced Learners Activity
- Enrich (in the *Chapter Resources*)
- Extend the Project
- **ELL** Activity

GO DIGITAL
- HMH Mega Math
- *i*Tools

WHAT ARE THE OTHER CHILDREN DOING?

Grab-and-Go!™

Differentiated Centers Kit

The kit provides literature, games, and activities for use every day.

Strategies for
English Language Learners

The Model Concepts Strategy uses models, role-playing, and pictures as instructional lifelines to support comprehension by providing experiences and images that children can draw upon when learning new concepts.

by Elizabeth Jiménez
CEO, GEMAS Consulting
Professional Expert on
English Language Learner Education
Bilingual Education and Dual Language
Pomona, California

Benefit to English Language Learners

Teachers can use models, step-by-step visuals, and role-playing to explain concepts to English Language Learners. It is beneficial to English Language Learners because:

- having the physical or visual manifestation of the actions removes the barrier of language and aids comprehension.

- English Language Learners are able to confirm their understanding with actions before having to speak.

- it engages all children in the lesson.

> **"**Modeling gives students a more concrete understanding and lays a foundation for later mastery of the task or process.**"**
>
> Rea, D.M. & Mercuri, S.P. 2006. *Research-based Strategies for English Language Learners.* Portsmouth, NH: Heineman

Planning for Instruction

English Language Learners need several opportunities to understand a new concept or to see how a new process is carried out. Modeling a mathematical process using counters, connecting cubes, fraction circles, base-ten blocks, or other manipulatives demonstrates the process in a way that does not rely on language. Children can focus on what is being explained before having to learn the vocabulary to explain it.

When modeling, teachers should confirm understanding of each step of the process before moving on to the next step. Children can sketch what teachers have modeled or demonstrate understanding by performing the same actions with their own models.

In addition to using common math manipulatives, teachers can model concepts by:

- color-coding examples to make it easier for children to focus precisely on what the teacher is explaining,

- having children act out a scene in a word problem (which can aid in understanding of problem situations in addition to understanding math), or

- drawing a process step-by-step and labeling each step.

Having a physical or visual example provides additional clues for English Language Learners to understand the meaning of problem situations and improve comprehension of mathematical processes. Modeling can also allow English Language Learners to demonstrate their understanding of math topics before they develop the vocabulary to fully express their thoughts in English.

Linguistic Note

Point out the difference between *how much* and *how many*. For example, when studying money, *How much do you have* is asking for a total value, while *How many coins do you have* is asking for a specific number of each coin.

Developing Math Language

sums the answers to addition problems

addends any of the numbers that are added

differences the answers to subtraction problems

 Visualize It
Have children make and complete this chart for each new vocabulary word as they go through the chapter.

Word	
Meaning	
Example	

 GO DIGITAL
- Interactive Student Edition
- Multimedia eGlossary

See **ELL** *Activity Guide for leveled activities.*

Objective Understand the math term *addend*.

Materials Vocabulary Card: *addend* (see *eTeacher Resources*)

Display several addition facts on the board. Explain that the numbers that are added are called *addends* and show the vocabulary card *addend*. Then have children point to each of the addends in the addition facts. Give children a word problem. Have them name the addends in the fact that solves the word problem.

Practice vocabulary by using questioning strategies such as the following:

Beginning
- Show children an addition fact. Have children point to the addends.

Intermediate
- What are the addends in 5 + 7 = 12? 5 and 7

Advanced
- When adding 8 + 3 + 2 = 13, what are the addends? 8, 3, 2 Have children write a different problem with three addends.

Vocabulary Strategy • Graphic Organizer

Materials **K.I.M. Diagram** (see *eTeacher Resources*)
- Write the vocabulary word in the left column.
- Write information about the word in the center column.
- Have children draw a picture, a memory clue, in the right column.

K Key Idea	I Information	M Memory Clue
sums		
addends		
differences		

Review Prerequisite Skills

TIER 2

Math Mountains!

Objective Practice addition and subtraction facts to 10.

Materials Math Mountain Cards for facts to 10 (see *eTeacher Resources*)

- Draw an example of a Math Mountain Card on the board. Ask children to describe what they notice about the card.
  - **What is the greatest number on the card?** 5 **Where is this number on the mountain?** on the top

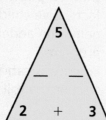

Math Expressions Model from *Math Expressions*. For more information visit **www.eduplace.com/hmhschool/mathexpressions**

- **How are the numbers at the bottom of the card related to 5?** They can be added together to make 5.
- **Why is the plus sign at the bottom?** The two numbers on the bottom can be added to make the number on the top. **Why are the minus signs on each side?** Each number on the bottom can be subtracted from the number on the top of the card to get the other number on the card.
- Have children practice addition and subtraction facts with the cards.

TIER 3

Hop on the Line!

Objective Practice counting on and counting back for addition and subtraction facts to 10.

Materials floor number line, labeled 0–10

- Explain to children that they will use the number line to count on to add. They will stand next to the number line and hop from number to number.
- Tell children they will add 6 and 2. Ask a volunteer to act out the addition as the class answers these questions.

What number should [child's name] start on? 6

How many spaces should [child's name] hop? 2 spaces

Where will [child's name] land? on 8

What number sentence did [child's name] model? $6 + 2 = 8$

- Ask all the children to write the number sentence.
- Continue the activity with different addition facts, adding 1, 2, or 3 to show sums to 10.
- Then repeat the activity for subtraction facts with start numbers to 10 and have a child begin on a number and hop to model counting back by 1, 2, or 3.

Operations and Algebraic Thinking

Making Content Connections

Across Grades

Before Grade 2, children represented and solved addition and subtraction problems (1.OA.A). The foundation, knowledge, and skills gained from working with addition and subtraction problems within 20, and the understanding of place value and properties of operations, prepared children for work with addition and subtraction problems within 100 (1.NBT.C). The addition and subtraction concepts, strategies, and skills taught in Grade 1 helped children build a foundation of conceptual understanding, strategic reasoning, and problem solving leading to mastery in addition and subtraction (1.OA.C).

In Grade 2, children extend their understanding of addition and subtraction. In Chapter 3, children continue to learn how to add and subtract within 20 using various strategies (2.OA.B), which will help prepare them for future work with multi-digit addition and subtraction. They use their knowledge of addition facts to better understand the inverse relationship between addition and subtraction. In later chapters, children will use skills from Chapter 3 as they solve two- and three-digit addition and subtraction word problems (2.NBT.B).

After Grade 2, children will learn how patterns in repeated addition and repeated subtraction can be used to explain the operations of multiplication and division (3.OA.D). They will represent and solve multiplication and division word problems (3.OA.A) and will solve problems involving the four operations (3.OA.D).

Connect to the Major Work

Representing and solving addition and subtraction problems is part of the major work in Grade 2 (2.OA.A). Children also use place value understanding and properties of operations to add and subtract (2.NBT.A). Chapter 3 provides children with many opportunities to connect the content to the major work. Exercises found in Lessons 3.1–3.7 focus on building fluency in addition and subtraction within 20 (2.OA.B.2), while exercises in Lessons 3.8 and 3.9 focus on solving addition and subtraction problems within 100 (2.OA.A.1). Children apply this knowledge to construct a full comprehension of addition and subtraction.

Common Core State Standards Across the Grades

Before

Domain: **Operations and Algebraic Thinking**

Cluster A: Represent and solve problems involving addition and subtraction.
Standard: **1.OA.A.1**

Cluster C: Add and subtract within 20.
Standards: **1.OA.C.5, 1.OA.C.6**

Grade 2

Domain: **Operations and Algebraic Thinking**

▉ Cluster A: Represent and solve problems involving addition and subtraction.
Standard: **2.OA.A.1**

▉ Cluster B: Add and subtract within 20.
Standard: **2.OA.B.1**

☐ Cluster C: Work with equal groups of objects to gain foundations for multiplication.
Standard: **2.OA.C.4**

After

Domain: **Operations and Algebraic Thinking**

Cluster A: Represent and solve problems involving multiplication and division.
Standard: **3.OA.A.1**

Cluster D: Solve problems involving the four operations, and identify and explain patterns in arithmetic.
Standard: **3.OA.D.8**

For the full text of the Common Core State Standards, see the A page of each lesson or the *Common Core State Standards Correlations* in the *Planning Guide*.
For the full text of the Standards for Mathematical Practices, see *Mathematical Practices in GO Math!* in the *Planning Guide*.

Chapter 3

Introduce the Chapter

Parrot fish live near coral reefs in tropical ocean waters. They use their sharp teeth to scrape food off of the coral.

Suppose 10 parrot fish are eating at a coral reef. 3 of the fish swim away. How many fish are still eating? 7 fish

Explore with children some ways to solve the problem. Encourage children to make a variety of suggestions. Then have them work in small groups and use a strategy of their choice to solve.

Additional Facts About Parrot Fish

- Parrot fish have grinding teeth in their throats. They use these teeth to get to food hidden inside the chunks of coral they take from reefs.

- A group of fish is called a school.

Discussion Question

- **Have you ever seen a colorful fish? If you have, describe what it looked like. Where did you see it?** Answers will vary.

Chapter 3 Basic Facts and Relationships

Parrot fish live near coral reefs in tropical ocean waters. They use their sharp teeth to scrape food off of the coral.

Suppose 10 parrot fish are eating at a coral reef. 3 of the fish swim away. How many fish are still eating?

Chapter 3   one hundred fifty-nine **159**

Intervention Options  Response to Intervention

Use Show What You Know, Lesson Quick Check, and Assessments to diagnose children's intervention levels.

TIER 1	TIER 2	TIER 3	ENRICHMENT
On-Level Intervention	**Strategic Intervention**	**Intensive Intervention**	**Independent Activities**
For children who are generally at grade level but need early intervention with the lesson concepts, use:	For children who need small group instruction to review concepts and skills needed for the chapter, use:	For children who need one-on-one instruction to build foundational skills for the chapter, use:	For children who successfully complete lessons, use:

TIER 1:
- Reteach (in the *Chapter Resources*)
- Personal Math Trainer
- Tier 1 Activity online

TIER 2:
- Strategic Intervention Guide
- Personal Math Trainer
- Prerequisite Skills Activities
- Tier 2 Activity online

TIER 3:
- Intensive Intervention Guide
- Personal Math Trainer
- Prerequisite Skills Activities

ENRICHMENT: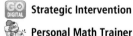
Differentiated Centers Kit
- Advanced Learners Activity for every lesson
- Enrich Activity (in the *Chapter Resources*)
- HMH Mega Math

159   Chapter 3

Name _____

 **Show What You Know** 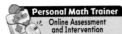 **Personal Math Trainer**
Online Assessment and Intervention

Use Symbols to Add

Use the picture. Use + and = to complete
the addition sentence. (K.OA.A.5)

1. 🍎🍎🍎 🍏   3 ⊕ 1 ⊜ 4

2. ⭐⭐☆☆☆   2 ⊕ 3 ⊜ 5

Sums to 10

Write the sum. (1.OA.C.6)

3. 4	4. 5	5. 2	6. 6	7. 9
+3	+0	+7	+2	+1
7	5	9	8	10

Doubles and Doubles Plus One

Write the addition sentence. (1.OA.C.6)

8.   9.

3 ⊕ 3 ⊜ 6   3 ⊕ 4 ⊜ 7

This page checks understanding of important skills needed
for success in Chapter 3.

160 one hundred sixty

© Houghton Mifflin Harcourt Publishing Company • Image Credits: (tcl) ©PhotoAlto/Getty Images

 Show What You Know • Diagnostic Assessment

Use to determine if children need intervention for the chapter's prerequisite skills.

Were children successful with Show What You Know?

If NO...then INTERVENE

If YES...then use INDEPENDENT ACTIVITIES

	Skill	Missed More Than	Personal Math Trainer	Intervene With
TIER 3	Use Symbols to Add	0	K.OA.A.5	*Intensive Intervention* Skill 2; *Intensive Intervention User Guide* Activity 3
TIER 2	Sums to 10	1	1.OA.C.6	*Strategic Intervention* Skill 5
TIER 2	Doubles and Doubles Plus One	0	1.OA.C.6	*Strategic Intervention* Skill 6

Grab-and-Go!™

Differentiated Centers Kit

Use the Enrich Activity in *the Chapter Resources* or the independent activities in the *Grab-and-Go™ Differentiated Centers Kit.*

Assessing Prior Knowledge

Have children complete on their own **Show What You Know.** Tested items are the prerequisite skills of this chapter.

Diagnostic Interview Task

The alternative interview tasks below evaluate children's understanding of each **Show What You Know** skill. The diagnostic chart may be used for intervention on prerequisite skills.

Materials two-color counters, connecting cubes

For evaluation checklist see *Chapter Resource Book.*

Display one blue connecting cube and a train of two red connecting cubes.

- Have the child write a number sentence to show the addition of the cubes. 1 + 2 = 3

Place 4 red counters and 2 yellow counters in front of the child.

- Have the child find the total number of counters. 6 counters

Display two trains of 4 red connecting cubes.

- Have the child write the doubles fact that is modeled with the cubes. 4 + 4 = 8

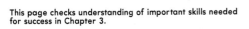

Chapter 3

Vocabulary Builder

Have children complete the activities on this page by working alone or with partners.

▶ **Visualize It** Make sure children understand that they should sort the Review Words and record them in the Venn diagram. Have children share how they sorted the words and tell how they decided to place each one.

▶ **Understand Vocabulary**

You may want to remind children that addition sentences have a plus sign and subtraction sentences have a minus sign.

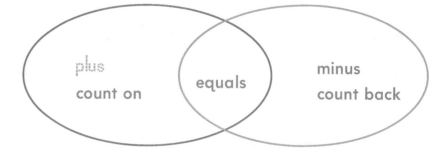

Name _____

Vocabulary Builder

Review Words
addition
subtraction
plus
minus
equals
count on
count back

Visualize It
Sort the review words in the graphic organizer.

Addition Words   **Subtraction** Words

plus
count on

 equals

minus
count back

Understand Vocabulary

1. Circle the **addition** sentence. $3 + 6 = 9$ $9 - 6 = 3$

2. Circle the **subtraction** sentence. $8 + 2 = 10$ $10 - 2 = 8$

3. Circle the **count on** fact. $5 - 1 = 4$ $4 + 1 = 5$

4. Circle the **count back** fact. $8 - 2 = 6$ $6 + 2 = 8$

© Houghton Mifflin Harcourt Publishing Company

Chapter 3

GO DIGITAL • Interactive Student Edition • Multimedia eGlossary

one hundred sixty-one **161**

Vocabulary Preview

Preview with children the following words that will be used in this chapter.

sums   **addends**   **differences**

For each preview word, have children try to give the meaning of the word on their own. If they have difficulty, give them a sentence using the word in a context so that its meaning can be determined. Once children have given a correct meaning, have them explain which words in the sentence you gave helped them know the meaning.

Vocabulary Cards

Children can enhance their understanding of **key chapter vocabulary** through the use of the vocabulary cards found in the Student Edition.

Have children cut out the cards and create their own deck of terms. You can use these cards to **reinforce knowledge** and **reading across the content areas**.

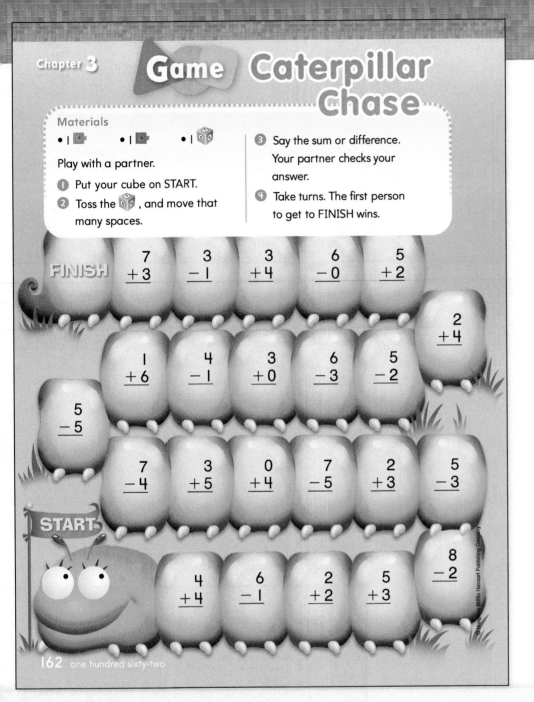

Chapter 3

Game Caterpillar Chase

Materials

• 1 • 1 • 1

Play with a partner.

1. Put your cube on START.
2. Toss the , and move that many spaces.
3. Say the sum or difference. Your partner checks your answer.
4. Take turns. The first person to get to FINISH wins.

FINISH

| $\begin{array}{r}7\\+3\\\hline\end{array}$ | $\begin{array}{r}3\\-1\\\hline\end{array}$ | $\begin{array}{r}3\\+4\\\hline\end{array}$ | $\begin{array}{r}6\\-0\\\hline\end{array}$ | $\begin{array}{r}5\\+2\\\hline\end{array}$ |

$\begin{array}{r}2\\+4\\\hline\end{array}$

| $\begin{array}{r}1\\+6\\\hline\end{array}$ | $\begin{array}{r}4\\-1\\\hline\end{array}$ | $\begin{array}{r}3\\+0\\\hline\end{array}$ | $\begin{array}{r}6\\-3\\\hline\end{array}$ | $\begin{array}{r}5\\-2\\\hline\end{array}$ |

$\begin{array}{r}5\\-5\\\hline\end{array}$

| $\begin{array}{r}7\\-4\\\hline\end{array}$ | $\begin{array}{r}3\\+5\\\hline\end{array}$ | $\begin{array}{r}0\\+4\\\hline\end{array}$ | $\begin{array}{r}7\\-5\\\hline\end{array}$ | $\begin{array}{r}2\\+3\\\hline\end{array}$ | $\begin{array}{r}5\\-3\\\hline\end{array}$ |

START

| $\begin{array}{r}4\\+4\\\hline\end{array}$ | $\begin{array}{r}6\\-1\\\hline\end{array}$ | $\begin{array}{r}2\\+2\\\hline\end{array}$ | $\begin{array}{r}5\\+3\\\hline\end{array}$ |

$\begin{array}{r}8\\-2\\\hline\end{array}$

Houghton Mifflin Harcourt Publishing Company

162 one hundred sixty-two

Chapter Resources

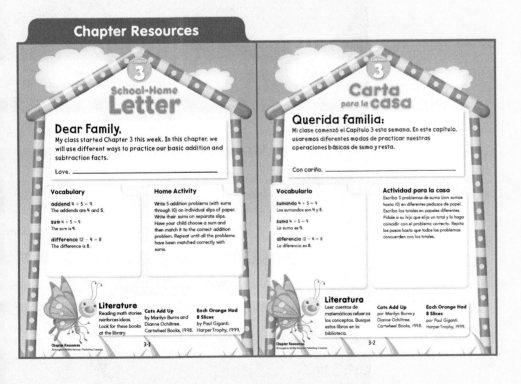

School-Home Letter

Dear Family,
My class started Chapter 3 this week. In this chapter, we will use different ways to practice our basic addition and subtraction facts.

Love, _____

Vocabulary

addend 4 + 5 = 9
The addends are 4 and 5.

sum 4 + 5 = 9
The sum is 9.

difference 12 − 4 = 8
The difference is 8.

Home Activity

Write 5 addition problems (with sums through 10) on individual slips of paper. Write their sums on separate slips. Have your child choose a sum and then match it to the correct addition problem. Repeat until all the problems have been matched correctly with sums.

Literature
Reading math stories reinforces ideas. Look for these books at the library.

Cats Add Up
by Marilyn Burns and Dianne Ochiltree. Cartwheel Books, 1998.

Each Orange Had 8 Slices
by Paul Giganti. HarperTrophy, 1999.

Chapter Resources
© Houghton Mifflin Harcourt Publishing Company
3-1

Carta para la casa

Querida familia:
Mi clase comenzó el Capítulo 3 esta semana. En este capítulo, usaremos diferentes modos de practicar nuestras operaciones básicas de suma y resta.

Con cariño, _____

Vocabulario

sumando 4 + 5 = 9
Los sumandos son 4 y 5.

suma 4 + 5 = 9
La suma es 9.

diferencia 12 − 4 = 8
La diferencia es 8.

Actividad para la casa

Escriba 5 problemas de suma (con sumas hasta 10) en diferentes pedazos de papel. Escriba los totales en papeles diferentes. Pídale a su hijo que elija un total y lo haga coincidir con el problema correcto. Repita los pasos hasta que todos los problemas concuerden con los totales.

Literatura
Leer cuentos de matemáticas refuerza los conceptos. Busque estos libros en la biblioteca.

Cats Add Up
por Marilyn Burns y Dianne Ochiltree. Cartwheel Books, 1998.

Each Orange Had 8 Slices
por Paul Giganti. HarperTrophy, 1999.

Chapter Resources
© Houghton Mifflin Harcourt Publishing Company
3-2

Game Caterpillar Chase

▶ Using the Game

Materials number cube (labeled 1–6), 1 red connecting cube and 1 blue connecting cube, or other playing pieces

This activity gives children an opportunity to practice basic addition and subtraction facts. Partners take turns tossing the number cube and moving his or her playing piece that many spaces. The partner says the answer for the vertical addition or subtraction problem on the space on which he or she lands. The other partner then checks the answer. If it is correct, that player stays on the space. If the answer is incorrect, the player goes back to the space on which he or she started.

Partners take turns. The first partner to get to FINISH wins the game.

School-Home Letter available in English and Spanish in the *Chapter Resources*. Multiple languages available online at *www.thinkcentral.com*.

The letter provides families with an overview of the math in the chapter, math vocabulary, an activity, and literature to read together.

Basic Facts and Relationships   162

Going Places with *GO Math!* Words

Introduce the Words

Provide child-friendly examples and explanations for the words from this chapter, such as the ones below. Then ask volunteers to explain the math vocabulary in their own words.

- *Addends* are the numbers you add in an addition problem.
- The *difference* is the answer in a subtraction problem.
- The number 50 has two *digits*.
- 2, 4, and 6 are *even numbers*.
- 5 + 4 *is equal to* 4 + 5
- 3, 5, and 7 are *odd numbers*.
- Six *tens* make up 60.
- The *sum* of 15 and 24 is 39.

Math Journal  Math

Have children draw pictures or use numbers to show what the vocabulary words mean. Then ask them to discuss the words and pictures with a partner.

Going to a Coral Reef:

What You Need
Each group needs:

- number cube
- connecting cubes for playing pieces

Show children how to

- roll the number cube
- count and move the correct number of spaces.

ELL Discuss any game terms, such as roll a number cube, space, and playing piece, to insure that students understand their meanings.

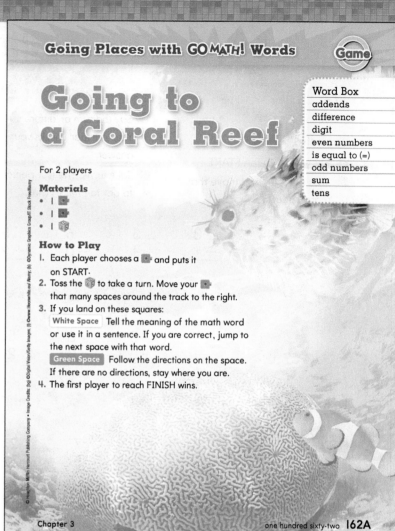

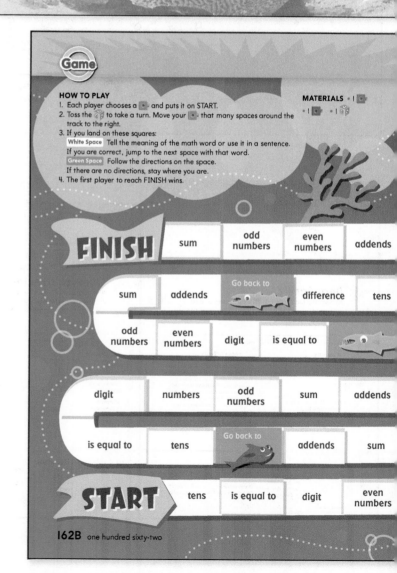

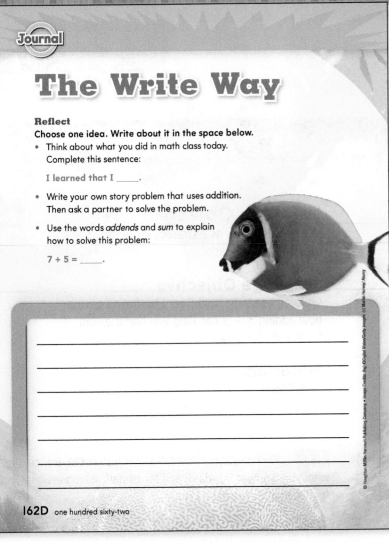

Journal

The Write Way

Reflect

Choose one idea. Write about it in the space below.

- Think about what you did in math class today. Complete this sentence:

  I learned that I _____.

- Write your own story problem that uses addition. Then ask a partner to solve the problem.

- Use the words *addends* and *sum* to explain how to solve this problem:

  7 + 5 = _____.

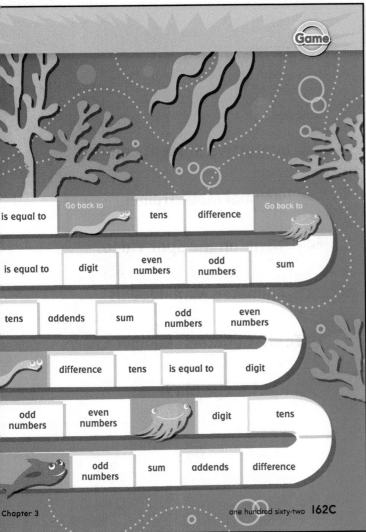

Game

is equal to	Go back to	tens	difference	Go back to
is equal to	digit	even numbers	odd numbers	sum
tens	addends	sum	odd numbers	even numbers
	difference	tens	is equal to	digit
odd numbers	even numbers		digit	tens
	odd numbers	sum	addends	difference

Play the Game

This game may be played before, during, or after the content is taught. Read the game directions with children. Then model how to play the game. Show children how to toss the number cube, read the number rolled, and move a playing piece that many spaces. Demonstrate what to do when a player lands on the different kinds of spaces. For a white space with a math term, model how to give the meaning of the term and use the term in a sentence. For a green space with directions, demonstrate how to follow them.

Be sure to explain how a player wins the game and ensure that all children understand how to play.

The directions for playing the game can also be found in the Chapter Resource book.

The Write Way

These short, informal writing activities address the vocabulary and content from this chapter. Communicating about math clarifies and deepens students' understandings about math concepts.

Read the writing prompts with students. Give them time to choose an idea and write about it. When students have completed their writing, ask them to share it and discuss these questions.

- **Does my writing show that I understand the math idea(s)?**
- **Do I use math words correctly?**
- **Is my writing clear and easy to follow?**
- **Do I use complete sentences? Are my grammar, spelling, and punctuation correct?**

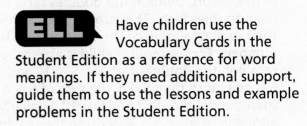

ELL Have children use the Vocabulary Cards in the Student Edition as a reference for word meanings. If they need additional support, guide them to use the lessons and example problems in the Student Edition.

Use Doubles Facts

LESSON AT A GLANCE

F C R Focus:

Common Core State Standards

2.OA.B.2 Fluently add and subtract within 20 using mental strategies. By end of Grade 2, know from memory all sums of two one-digit numbers.

MATHEMATICAL PRACTICES (See *Mathematical Practices in GO Math!* in the *Planning Guide* for full text.)
MP1 Make sense of problems and persevere in solving them. **MP4** Model with mathematics.
MP7 Look for and make use of structure. **MP8** Look for and express regularity in repeated reasoning.

F C R Coherence:

Standards Across the Grades

Before	Grade 2	After
1.OA.A.1	2.OA.B.2	3.OA.A.1
1.OA.A.2		

F C R Rigor:

Level 1: Understand Concepts...................*Share and Show* (✓ Checked Items)
Level 2: Procedural Skills and Fluency.......*On Your Own, Practice and Homework*
Level 3: Applications.................................*Think Smarter and Go Deeper*

Learning Objective

Use doubles facts as a strategy for finding sums for near doubles facts.

Language Objective

Children use their MathBoard to show a partner how adding 3 + 3 can help you find the sum for 3 + 4.

Materials

MathBoard

F C R For more about how *GO Math!* fosters **Coherence** within the Content Standards and Mathematical Progressions for this chapter, see page 159J.

About the Math

Professional Development

Progress to Algebra
Why Teach This?

In this chapter, various strategies are reviewed and reinforced in order for children to achieve fluency with the basic facts.

In this lesson, children use doubles facts to find sums for near doubles facts. This strategy helps children develop their understanding of the relationships between numbers. For example, a child is able to solve 5 + 6 by recalling the doubles fact 5 + 5 = 10 and recognizing that 6 is one more than 5. So, the sum of 5 + 6 is one more than the doubles fact 5 + 5 = 10. Similarly, children are also able to solve 5 + 4 because they understand that 4 is one less than 5. As children become fluent in the application of the doubles fact strategy, they strengthen their mental math skills.

 Professional Development Videos

 GO DIGITAL

 **Interactive Student Edition**

 **Personal Math Trainer**

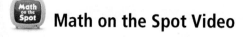 **Math on the Spot Video**

 **Animated Math Models**

 **iTools: Counters; Number Charts**

MM HMH Mega Math

① ENGAGE

with the Interactive Student Edition

Essential Question

How can you use doubles facts to find sums for near doubles facts?

Making Connections

Ask children what they know about doubles facts.

When have you used doubles facts before? Sample answer: When representing even numbers. **How do you represent a doubles fact with counting cubes?** by making two trains of the same length

Learning Activity

What is the problem the children are trying to solve? Connect the story to the problem. Ask the following questions.

- **What doubles facts are the children using?** Check children's work.

- **Is it possible for the sum of a doubles fact to be odd?** No. **Explain.** Sample answer: since both addends are the same, a picture of each addend would have the same number of ones, and each addend would show pairs with no cubes left over.

Literacy and Mathematics

View the lesson opener with the children. Then, choose one or more of the following activities:

- Have children write a story involving at least three doubles facts. Have them circle the doubles facts in their story.

- Have children represent doubles facts from $1 + 1$ to $9 + 9$ using connecting cubes. Have them draw quick pictures to represent each sum.

② EXPLORE

Listen and Draw 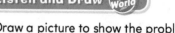 MATHEMATICAL PRACTICES

MP4 Model with mathematics. Read the following problem aloud.

Nathan has 6 toy cars. Alisha gives him 6 more toy cars. How many toy cars does Nathan have now?

Then have children draw a picture on the page to represent the problem. Suggest that children draw simple shapes, such as circles or Xs, to stand for toy cars.

- **Describe what you drew to show the problem.** Possible answer: I drew two groups of six toy cars.

- **What is the problem that you are solving?** how many toy cars Nathan has now

Have children use their drawings to write an addition sentence.

- **What addition sentence did you write? Describe the numbers being added in your number sentence.** 6 + 6 = 12. The numbers being added are the same. The numbers being added are even; each shows pairs with no cubes left over.

- **What are some other doubles facts that you know?** Some possible answers: 1 + 1 = 2; 2 + 2 = 4; 3 + 3 = 6; 4 + 4 = 8; 5 + 5 = 10; 7 + 7 = 14; 8 + 8 = 16; 9 + 9 = 18

 MP4 Model with mathematics. Use Math Talk to focus on children's understanding of why certain facts are called doubles facts.

 Strategy: Illustrate Understanding

Point out that in a doubles fact the numbers being added are the same.

- **Read the following problem:** Benji has 4 flowers. Mary has 4 flowers. How many flowers do they have in all?

- **Have children make a drawing that shows Benji's flowers and Mary's flowers by drawing two groups in two rows. Have them use a different color for each person's flowers.**

- **Point out the one-to-one correspondence in the drawing. Have children explain their drawing.**

- **Then have children write an addition sentence to show the number of flowers in all.**

163 Chapter 3

2.OA.B.2 Fluently add and subtract within 20 using mental strategies. By end of Grade 2, know from memory all sums of two one-digit numbers.
Progress to Algebra

Name _____

Lesson 3.1

Use Doubles Facts

Essential Question How can you use doubles facts to find sums for near doubles facts?

Common Core **Operations and Algebraic Thinking—2.OA.B.2**
MATHEMATICAL PRACTICES
MP1, MP4, MP7

Listen and Draw

Draw a picture to show the problem. Then write an addition sentence for the problem.

Check children's drawings.

Problem Type:
Add To • Result Unknown

$$\underline{6} \enspace \oplus \enspace \underline{6} \enspace \ominus \enspace \underline{12}$$

Math Talk: Possible answer: When you add two numbers that are the same, it is like doubling that number.

$$\underline{12} \text{ toy cars}$$

FOR THE TEACHER • Read this problem and have children draw a picture for the problem. Nathan has 6 toy cars. Alisha gives him 6 more toy cars. How many toy cars does Nathan have now? After children write an addition sentence, have them name other doubles facts that they know.

Math Talk MATHEMATICAL PRACTICES 4
Represent Explain why 4 + 4 = 8 is called a doubles fact.

Chapter 3

one hundred sixty-three **163**

Reteach 3.1 ▲ RtI

Name _____
Lesson 3.1 Reteach

Use Doubles Facts

Use doubles facts to help you find sums.

If you know 6 + 6, you can find 6 + 7.

$$\underline{6} + \underline{6} = \underline{12}$$

7 is 1 more than 6. So 6 + 7 is 1 more than 6 + 6.

$$\underline{6} + \underline{7} = \underline{13}$$

Write a doubles fact you can use to find the sum. Write the sum.

Doubles facts may vary. Check children's work.

1. 4 + 5 = __9__   ___ + ___ = ___

2. 5 + 6 = __11__   ___ + ___ = ___

3. 7 + 8 = __15__   ___ + ___ = ___

4. 8 + 9 = __17__   ___ + ___ = ___

Chapter Resources
3-5
Reteach

Enrich 3.1 — Differentiated Instruction

Name _____
Lesson 3.1 Enrich

What Number Am I?

Use doubles facts to solve. Write the number.

1. I am one more than the sum of the doubles fact for 2. What number am I?
__5__

2. I am one less than the sum of the doubles fact for 4. What number am I?
__7__

3. I am one less than the sum of the doubles fact for 6. What number am I?
__11__

4. I am one more than the sum of the doubles fact for 5. What number am I?
__11__

5. I am one more than the sum of the doubles fact for 3. What number am I?
__7__

6. I am one less than the sum of the doubles fact for 9. What number am I?
__17__

Writing and Reasoning Are your answers odd numbers or even numbers? Explain how you know.

Odd. Possible explanation: The sums of doubles are always even. If you add or subtract 1, you make an odd number.

Chapter Resources
3-6
Enrich

Model and Draw

You can use doubles facts to find sums for other facts.

3 + 4 = ?
↓
3 + 3 + 1 = ?

3 + 3 = 6

6 + 1 = 7

So, 3 + 4 = __7__.

7 + 6 = ?
↓
7 + 7 − 1 = ?

7 + 7 = 14

14 − 1 = 13

So, 7 + 6 = __13__.

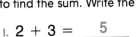 **Share and Show**

Write a doubles fact you can use to find the sum. Write the sum.

Doubles facts may vary. Check children's work.

1. 2 + 3 = __5__

____ + ____ = ____

2. 4 + 5 = __9__

____ + ____ = ____

3. 4 + 3 = __7__

____ + ____ = ____

4. 6 + 7 = __13__

____ + ____ = ____

5. 5 + 6 = __11__

____ + ____ = ____

6. 8 + 7 = __15__

____ + ____ = ____

© Houghton Mifflin Harcourt Publishing Company

Model and Draw Common Core MATHEMATICAL PRACTICES

MP7 Look for and make use of structure. Work through the model with children.

- **Why can 3 + 4 be written as 3 + 3 + 1?**
  Possible answer: 4 is the same as one more than 3.
- **Why can 7 + 6 be written as 7 + 7 − 1?**
  Possible answer: 6 is the same as one less than 7.
- **Can you write 3 + 4 as 4 + 4 − 1? Explain.**
  Yes; Possible answer: 3 is the same as one less than 4.

③ EXPLAIN

Share and Show MATH BOARD

Connect Exercises 1–6 to the learning model.

- **In Exercise 1, which doubles fact did you use? Explain your choice.** Possible answer: I used 2 + 2 = 4 because 2 is a number in the problem. Then I added one more because 3 is one more than 2.

Use the checked exercises for **Quick Check**. Children should use their MathBoards to show their solutions to these exercises.

✓ Quick Check  RtI

| If | a child misses the checked exercises |
| Then | **Differentiate Instruction** with |

- Reteach 3.1
- Personal Math trainer 2.OA.B.2
- RtI Tier 1 Activity (online)

⚠ COMMON ERRORS

Error Children may not understand when to add 1 or subtract 1 from the doubles fact.

Example In Exercise 3, children write 4 + 3 = 9.

Springboard to Learning Have children write a doubles fact they can use to find the sum for a given problem. Then have them circle the number in the problem that is not in the doubles fact. Ask children if the number that they circled is 1 more or 1 less than each of the numbers being added in the doubles fact.

Advanced Learners 🕐 Kinesthetic / Interpersonal Partners

Materials sets of Numeral Cards 2–9 (see *eTeacher Resources*)

- Have one child choose a card. Have the other child name the number 1 greater than or 1 less than that number.
- Have children use the numbers to write two addition problems. For example, with a 4-card and the number 5, children would write 4 + 5 = ____ and 5 + 4 = ____.
- Each partner takes one of the problems. Then they each use two different doubles facts to find the sum of their problem in two ways.

5 + 4 = ____
5 + 5 − 1 = 9
4 + 4 + 1 = 9

4 ELABORATE

On Your Own

If a child answers the checked exercises correctly, assign Exercises 7–15.

Point out that children should write the sum on the line next to the given problem. On the lines below the problem, they should write the doubles fact that they used.

 THINK SMARTER

Children must use the clues given to find a doubles fact that Mr. Norris might have written. Ask early finishers to write a similar riddle and have them exchange with a partner to solve.

 Math on the Spot Video Tutor

Use this video to help children model and solve this type of *Think Smarter* problem.

GO DIGITAL Math on the Spot videos are in the Interactive Student Edition and at *www.thinkcentral.com*.

GO DEEPER

MP8 Look for and express regularity in repeated reasoning.

- Give children the doubles fact 5 + 5 = 10. Have them use this doubles fact to write two near doubles facts. 5 + 6 = 11; 5 + 4 = 9. Ask children to explain how they found their answers. Then have them repeat the activity for the doubles fact 4 + 4 = 8. 4 + 5 = 9; 4 + 3 = 7.

- **What do you notice about the answers?** All the answers are odd, they show pairs with one cube left over.

Additional Example
Add To • Start Unknown

- Brenna has some marbles. Then her brother gives her 6 more marbles. Now she has 15 marbles. How many marbles did Brenna have to start? 9 marbles

---

Name _____

On Your Own

Write a doubles fact you can use to find the sum. Write the sum. Doubles facts may vary. Check children's work.

7. $5 + 4 = \underline{\quad 9 \quad}$

_____ + _____ = _____

8. $6 + 5 = \underline{\quad 11 \quad}$

_____ + _____ = _____

9. $6 + 7 = \underline{\quad 13 \quad}$

_____ + _____ = _____

10. $7 + 8 = \underline{\quad 15 \quad}$

_____ + _____ = _____

11. $8 + 9 = \underline{\quad 17 \quad}$

_____ + _____ = _____

12. $5 + 6 = \underline{\quad 11 \quad}$

_____ + _____ = _____

13. $7 + 6 = \underline{\quad 13 \quad}$

_____ + _____ = _____

14. $9 + 8 = \underline{\quad 17 \quad}$

_____ + _____ = _____

15. **THINK SMARTER** Mr. Norris wrote a doubles fact. It has a sum greater than 6. The numbers that he added are each less than 6. What fact might he have written?

Children may write 4 + 4 = 8 or 5 + 5 = 10.

PROBLEM TYPE SITUATIONS

Addition and Subtraction

Put Together/Take Apart • Total Unknown
Exercises: 16, 17

Compare • Difference Unknown
Exercise: 17

Problem Solving · Applications   WRITE ▸ Math

Solve. Write or draw to explain.

16. **MATHEMATICAL PRACTICE ①** Analyze
Andrea has 8 red buttons and 9 blue buttons. How many buttons does Andrea have?

_____17_____ buttons

17. **GO DEEPER** Henry sees 3 rabbits. Callie sees double that number of rabbits. How many more rabbits does Callie see than Henry?

_____3_____ more rabbits

18. **THINK SMARTER** Could you use the doubles fact to find the sum for 4 + 5? Choose Yes or No.

$4 + 4 = 8$ ● Yes   ○ No

$5 + 5 = 10$ ● Yes   ○ No

$9 + 9 = 18$ ○ Yes   ● No

 TAKE HOME ACTIVITY · Ask your child to write three different doubles facts with sums less than 17.

© Houghton Mifflin Harcourt Publishing Company • Image Credits: (c) ©Getty Images/PhotoDisc

166 one hundred sixty-six

 DIFFERENTIATED INSTRUCTION | **INDEPENDENT ACTIVITIES**

Differentiated Centers Kit

Activities **Way to Go!**	*Literature* **Doubles Fun on the Farm**	*Games* **Caterpillar Chase**
		 Games
Children complete blue Activity Card 1 by using doubles to add.	Children read the book and add equal groups to make doubles.	Children practice basic addition facts to move along the game path.

Problem Solving · Applications
Common Core MATHEMATICAL PRACTICES

MP1 Make sense of problems and persevere in solving them. Have children read Exercise 16. Ask them to describe how they will solve the problem.

GO DEEPER

In Exercise 17, children use higher order thinking skills to find a doubles fact by using clues. If children need help starting, suggest that children make a list of doubles facts with addends up to 4.

THINK SMARTER

Children may not recognize that an even number of objects can represent a doubles fact. They should understand that an odd number of objects cannot represent a doubles fact.

⑤ EVALUATE   Formative Assessment

Essential Question

Reflect Using the Language Objective Have children use their MathBoard to demonstrate for a partner their answer to the Essential Question.

How can you use doubles facts to find sums for near doubles facts? Possible answer: If I know the sum of a doubles fact, I find the sum for a near doubles fact by comparing the numbers being added and deciding if I need to add 1 or subtract 1 from the sum of the doubles fact.

Math Journal   WRITE ▸ Math

Draw or write to show two ways to use a doubles fact to find 6 + 7.

Practice and Homework

Use the Practice and Homework pages to provide children with more practice of the concepts and skills presented in this lesson. Children master their understanding as they complete practice items and then challenge their critical thinking skills with Problem Solving. Use the Write Math section to determine children's understanding of content for this lesson. Encourage children to use their Math Journals to record their answers.

Use Doubles Facts

 COMMON CORE STANDARD—2.OA.B.2
Add and subtract within 20.

Write a doubles fact you can use to find the sum. Write the sum.

Doubles facts may vary. Check children's work.

1. $2 + 3 = \underline{5}$

 ___ + ___ = ___

2. $7 + 6 = \underline{13}$

 ___ + ___ = ___

3. $3 + 4 = \underline{7}$

 ___ + ___ = ___

4. $8 + 9 = \underline{17}$

 ___ + ___ = ___

Problem Solving (Real World)

Solve. Write or draw to explain.

5. There are 4 ants on a log. Then 5 ants crawl onto the log. How many ants are on the log now?

 $\underline{9}$ ants

6. **WRITE** Math Draw or write to show two ways to use a doubles fact to find $6 + 7$.

 _____

 _____

 Check children's work.

Cross-Curricular   S.T.E.M.

- Explain to children that living things have different needs. Animals and plants are living things with some of the same needs, such as water and air. Animals have other needs, such as food and shelter. The needs of plants also include light and nutrients from the soil.
- Have children name 6 animals and 5 plants. Ask them to find how many living things in all are in the two lists. 11 living things

SOCIAL STUDIES

Materials posterboard, markers

- Discuss with children the importance of rules in the classroom and at school. Explain that rules help people stay safe. For example, it is a rule not to run in the hallways so people do not get hurt.
- Have children list 3 safety rules for the classroom and 4 safety rules for the school. Ask them to find how many rules in all are in the two lists. 7 rules
- You may wish to have children make posters with the rules that can be displayed.

Lesson Check (2.OA.B.2)   Doubles facts may vary. Check children's work.

1. Write a doubles fact you can use to find the sum. Write the sum.

$$4 + 3 = \underline{\;7\;}$$

$$\underline{\qquad} + \underline{\qquad} = \underline{\qquad}$$

2. Write a doubles fact you can use to find the sum. Write the sum.

$$6 + 7 = \underline{\;13\;}$$

$$\underline{\qquad} + \underline{\qquad} = \underline{\qquad}$$

Spiral Review (2.OA.C.3, 2.NBT.A.1, 2.NBT.A.3, 2.NBT.A.4)

3. There are 451 children in Lia's school. Write a number greater than 451.

Possible answer: $\underline{511}$

4. What number is shown with these blocks?

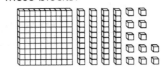

$\underline{152}$

5. Write a number with the digit 8 in the tens place.

Possible answer: $\underline{483}$

6. Circle the sum that is an even number.

$$2 + 3 = 5$$
$$3 + 4 = 7$$
$$4 + 5 = 9$$
$$\boxed{6 + 6 = 12}$$

FOR MORE PRACTICE
GO TO THE
Personal Math Trainer

© Houghton Mifflin Harcourt Publishing Company

168 one hundred sixty-eight

Continue concepts and skills practice with Lesson Check. Use Spiral Review to engage children in previously taught concepts and to promote content retention. Common Core standards are correlated to each section.

S.T.E.M. Connecting Math and Science

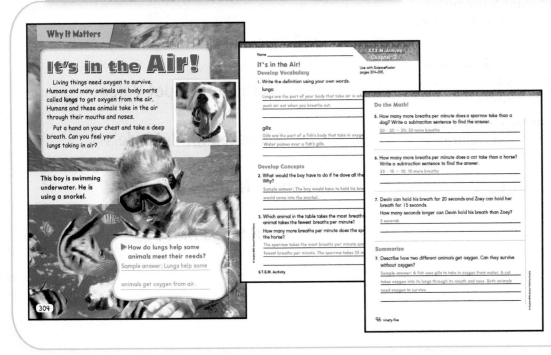

In Chapter 3, children extend their understanding of basic facts and the relationship between addition and subtraction, by practicing subtraction facts. These same topics are often used in the development of various science concepts and process skills.

Help children make the connection between math and science through the S.T.E.M. activities and activity worksheets found at www.thinkcentral. com. In Chapter 3, children connect math and science with the S.T.E.M. Activity *It's in the Air!* and the accompanying worksheets (pages 95 and 96).

Through this S.T.E.M. Activity, children will connect the *GO Math!* Chapter 3 concepts and skills with the breathing rates of various animals by finding the difference between the breathing rates of two animals. It is recommended that this S.T.E.M. Activity be used after Lesson 3.7.

Lesson 3.1 168

Practice Addition Facts

LESSON AT A GLANCE

FOCUS   COHERENCE   RIGOR

F C R Focus:

Common Core State Standards

2.OA.B.2 Fluently add and subtract within 20 using mental strategies. By end of Grade 2, know from memory all sums of two one-digit numbers.

MATHEMATICAL PRACTICES (See *Mathematical Practices in GO Math!* in the *Planning Guide* for full text.)
MP1 Make sense of problems and persevere in solving them. **MP7** Look for and make use of structure. **MP8** Look for and express regularity in repeated reasoning.

F C R Coherence:

Standards Across the Grades

Before	Grade 2	After
1.OA.A.1	2.OA.B.2	3.OA.D.8
1.OA.C.6		

F C R Rigor:

Level 1: Understand Concepts....................*Share and Show* (✓ Checked Items)
Level 2: Procedural Skills and Fluency.......*On Your Own, Practice and Homework*
Level 3: Applications................................*Think Smarter and Go Deeper*

Learning Objective
Recall sums for basic facts using properties and strategies.

Language Objective
Children recommend to a partner two great ways to remember sums.

Materials
MathBoard

F C R For more about how *GO Math!* fosters **Coherence** within the Content Standards and Mathematical Progressions for this chapter, see page 159J..

About the Math
Professional Development

Progress to Algebra
Why Teach This?

In this lesson, children will learn that changing the order of the addends does not change the sum. This is known as the Commutative Property of Addition.

At this age, understanding that 3 + 4 and 4 + 3 have the same sum helps to build fluency by reducing the number of facts that children need to commit to memory.

As children advance in math, the Commutative Property of Addition becomes important again as it allows children to simplify equations with addition.

 Professional Development Videos

 GO DIGITAL

 SE Interactive Student Edition

 Personal Math Trainer

 Math on the Spot Video

 Animated Math Models

 iT iTools: Number Charts

MM HMH Mega Math

Daily Routines

 Problem of the Day 3.2

Number of the Day

9   5   6

Arrange the digits in any order to form a 3-digit number. Tell the place value of each digit.

Have children share their 3-digit numbers and describe the place value of each digit in the number.

Vocabulary addends

> GO DIGITAL
> • Interactive Student Edition
> • Multimedia eGlossary

Vocabulary Builder
Addends

Write the following addition facts on the board and read them aloud.

1 + 8 = 9
2 + 7 = 9
3 + 6 = 9

Have volunteers come to the board and circle the addends in each fact. Then have children write two addition facts on a sheet of paper. Challenge children to write addition facts that have different addends and the same sum. Ask children to circle the addends in their addition facts.

❶ ENGAGE

with the Interactive Student Edition

Essential Question

What are some ways to remember sums?

Making Connections

Ask children to tell what they know about adding numbers.

How are addition facts like 3 + 6 = 9 or 4 + 2 = 6 different from doubles facts? Sample answer: the addends are different in those facts but they are the same in doubles facts. **Have you used basic addition facts outside of math class?** Answers may vary. **How did you add the two numbers?** Sample answers: I counted up by the second number, I drew a picture of each addend and counted the total.

Learning Activity

What is the problem the children are trying to solve? Connect the story to the problem. Ask the following questions.

* **Is it possible for the sum of two numbers less than 10 to have a sum greater than 20? Explain.** No; check children's explanations.

* **Is the sum of the addition fact 8 + 2 the same as the sum of 2 + 8?** Yes.

Literacy and Mathematics

View the lesson opener with the children. Then, choose one or more of the following activities:

* Have children write a story involving at least three basic addition facts. Have children circle the addition facts in their story with a green crayon.

* Have children use two colors of connecting cubes to represent an addition fact. Have them draw the representation and write the addition fact.

② EXPLORE

Listen and Draw Real World · Common Core MATHEMATICAL PRACTICES

MP8 Look for and express regularity in repeated reasoning. Read the problem and ask a volunteer to retell the problem in his or her own words.

On Monday, Tony saw 3 dogs and 6 cats. How many animals did he see?

Have children draw a picture and write a number sentence for the problem in the top box. Then ask these questions.

- **How does your drawing show the problem?** Answers will vary, but should show an understanding of representing addition with a drawing.

- **How did you decide whether to write an addition or a subtraction sentence?** Possible answer: I wrote an addition sentence to show that I was combining the numbers of objects.

Then read the following problem. Have children draw a picture and write a number sentence for the problem in the bottom box.

On Tuesday, Tony saw 6 dogs and 3 cats. How many animals did he see?

 Math Talk **MP1 Make sense of problems and persevere in solving them.**

Use **Math Talk** to focus on children's understanding that when they use the Commutative Property of Addition to change the order of the addends, the sum does not change.

 ELL **Strategy:**
Model Concepts

Children may understand concepts, story problems, and vocabulary if they are illustrated or modeled.

- **Have children show 5 red cubes and add 7 blue cubes. What addition facts does your model show?** 5 + 7 = 12 and 7 + 5 = 12

- **Discuss with children how you can add numbers in any order and the sum does not change.**

169 Chapter 3

Name _____

Practice Addition Facts

Essential Question What are some ways to remember sums?

Lesson 3.2

Common Core **Operations and Algebraic Thinking—2.OA.B.2**
MATHEMATICAL PRACTICES
MP1, MP7, MP8

Listen and Draw Real World

Draw pictures to show the problems. Check children's drawings.

_____ 3 + 6 = 9 _____

Problem Type:
Put Together/Take Apart •
Total Unknown

Problem Type:
Put Together/Take Apart •
Total Unknown

Math Talk: Possible answer: In both problems, the sum is the same and the same two numbers are being added. The order of the numbers being added is different.

_____ 6 + 3 = 9 _____

 FOR THE TEACHER • Read the following two problems. Have children draw a picture and write a number sentence for each. On Monday, Tony saw 3 dogs and 6 cats. How many animals did he see? On Tuesday, Tony saw 6 dogs and 3 cats. How many animals did he see?

Math Talk MATHEMATICAL PRACTICES

Analyze Explain how the two problems are alike. Explain how they are different.

Chapter 3   one hundred sixty-nine **169**

Differentiated Instruction

Reteach 3.2 ▲ RtI

Name _____

Lesson 3.2 Reteach

Practice Addition Facts

Use what you know to find sums.

☆☆☆ ★★★★★
Add in any order.   3 + 5 = __8__
★★★★★ ☆☆☆
If you know 3 + 5,
then you know 5 + 3.   5 + 3 = __8__

☆☆☆☆☆ ★
Count on to add. To add 1, 2, or 3 to any
number, count on from that number.   5 + 1 = __6__

Write the sums.

1. 5 + 7 = __12__   2. __6__ = 5 + 1   3. 6 + 2 = __8__
   7 + 5 = __12__   __7__ = 5 + 2   6 + 3 = __9__

4. __14__ = 9 + 5   5. 7 + 3 = __10__   6. 5 + 2 = __7__
   __14__ = 5 + 9   3 + 7 = __10__   5 + 3 = __8__

7. __9__ = 3 + 6   8. 4 + 1 = __5__   9. 8 + 2 = __10__
   __9__ = 6 + 3   1 + 4 = __5__   8 + 3 = __11__

Chapter Resources   3-7   Reteach

Enrich 3.2

Name _____

Lesson 3.2 Enrich

Three in a Row

Write the sums in each box.
Draw a line through three boxes in a row that have one of the same sums.

9 + 0 = 9	6 + 0 = 6	5 + 0 = 5
0 + 7 = 7	0 + 8 = 8	0 + 2 = 2
5 + 5 = 10	4 + 4 = 8	3 + 3 = 6
5 + 4 = 9	4 + 5 = 9	3 + 4 = 7
7 + 4 = 11	6 + 6 = 12	6 + 3 = 9
4 + 7 = 11	6 + 5 = 11	3 + 6 = 9

7 + 8 = 15	9 + 2 = 11	4 + 4 = 8
8 + 7 = 15	2 + 9 = 11	4 + 3 = 7
9 + 9 = 18	0 + 0 = 0	5 + 2 = 7
9 + 8 = 17	4 + 0 = 4	2 + 5 = 7
9 + 9 = 18	6 + 6 = 12	6 + 1 = 7
9 + 10 = 19	6 + 7 = 13	1 + 6 = 7

 Writing and Reasoning Draw a loop around each box with number sentences that have 0 as an addend. Did you win again? Explain why.

Yes, the top row in the first puzzle has 3 number sentences in a row with zero as an addend.

Chapter Resources   3-8   Enrich

---

169   Chapter 3

Model and Draw

These are some ways to remember facts.

> You can count on 1, 2, or 3.

$6 + 1 = \underline{7}$
$6 + 2 = \underline{8}$
$6 + 3 = \underline{9}$

> Changing the order of the **addends** does not change the sum.

$\underline{8} = 2 + 6$
$\underline{8} = 6 + 2$

Share and Show

Write the sums.

1. $4 + 4 = \underline{8}$

   $4 + 5 = \underline{9}$

2. $5 + 0 = \underline{5}$

   $2 + 0 = \underline{2}$

3. $3 + 8 = \underline{11}$

   $8 + 3 = \underline{11}$

4. $\underline{10} = 5 + 5$

   $\underline{9} = 5 + 4$

5. $5 + 7 = \underline{12}$

   $7 + 5 = \underline{12}$

6. $\underline{14} = 7 + 7$

   $\underline{15} = 7 + 8$

7. $\underline{10} = 3 + 7$

   $\underline{10} = 7 + 3$

8. $9 + 3 = \underline{12}$

   $3 + 9 = \underline{12}$

9. $\underline{12} = 6 + 6$

   $\underline{11} = 6 + 5$

170 one hundred seventy

© Houghton Mifflin Harcourt Publishing Company

MP1 Make sense of problems and persevere in solving them. Work through the strategies and examples with children. For the first strategy, model counting on 1, 2, or 3. Then direct children's attention to the related facts.

- **When the addends in two facts are the same, why are the sums the same?**
  Possible answer: The same two numbers are being added together so the sum is the same.

③ EXPLAIN

Share and Show

Connect Exercises 1–9 to the learning model. Children can use the two modeled strategies to solve these problems.

- **Look at Exercise 2. Describe what happens when zero is added to a number.**
  Possible answer: When you add zero to a number, the sum is that number.

Use the checked exercises for **Quick Check**. Children should use their MathBoards to show their solutions to these exercises.

✓ Quick Check ▲ RtI

If	a child misses the checked exercises
Then	**Differentiate Instruction** with

- Reteach 3.2
- Personal Math trainer 2.OA.B.2
- RtI Tier 1 Activity (online)

Advanced Learners ⏱ Visual, Verbal / Linguistic — Partners

Materials Secret Code Cards 1–9 (front and back) (see *eTeacher Resources*)

- Have children work in pairs. One child shows the numeral side of a card and the dot side of another card. The other child writes an addition sentence using the numbers that the cards show as the addends.

- Ask children to describe how they found the sum. Then have children switch tasks and repeat the activity for a different pair of cards.

⚠ COMMON ERRORS

Error Children may not recognize the sum when it appears on the left of the equal sign.

Example In Exercise 4, children do not write the sum before the equal sign.

Springboard to Learning Remind children that number sentences can be written in different ways. Talk about how both sides of the equal sign must have the same value. Then have children write pairs of facts such as $4 + 3 = 7$ and $7 = 4 + 3$.

④ ELABORATE

On Your Own

If children answer Exercises 8 and 9 correctly, assign Exercises 10–22.

THINK SMARTER

Exercise 22 assesses children's ability to solve a multistep problem in a real-world context. Children must first find how many pictures Ellie painted using a doubles fact. Discuss with children that the word *twice* means double. Make sure children understand that this means Ellie painted twice as many pictures as Sam, not 2 pictures.

Then, children must find the total number of pictures that Sam and Ellie painted. Ask children to explain another way to solve the problem using skip counting.

Math on the Spot Video Tutor

Use this video to help children model and solve this type of *Think Smarter* problem.

GO DIGITAL Math on the Spot videos are in the Interactive Student Edition and at *www.thinkcentral.com*.

GO DEEPER

MP7 Look for and make use of structure

Write some addition problems (without sums) on the board. Have children identify a strategy they can use to find each sum. They may name one of the strategies or properties discussed in this lesson or the previous lesson, or they may describe another strategy. To encourage them to communicate mathematical ideas, have them discuss or draw a diagram to explain how the strategy helps them find the sum.

9 + 7	0 + 9	5 + 4
3 + 7	6 + 5	6 + 8

Name _____

On Your Own

Write the sums.

10. $7 + 1 = \underline{8}$ 11. $\underline{4} = 4 + 0$ 12. $5 + 5 = \underline{10}$

$1 + 7 = \underline{8}$ $\underline{9} = 9 + 0$ $5 + 4 = \underline{9}$

13. $8 + 2 = \underline{10}$ 14. $3 + 3 = \underline{6}$ 15. $7 + 8 = \underline{15}$

$2 + 8 = \underline{10}$ $3 + 4 = \underline{7}$ $8 + 7 = \underline{15}$

16. $\underline{5} = 4 + 1$ 17. $0 + 7 = \underline{7}$ 18. $8 + 8 = \underline{16}$

$\underline{5} = 1 + 4$ $0 + 6 = \underline{6}$ $8 + 9 = \underline{17}$

19. $5 + 3 = \underline{8}$ 20. $\underline{18} = 9 + 9$ 21. $6 + 7 = \underline{13}$

$3 + 5 = \underline{8}$ $\underline{17} = 9 + 8$ $7 + 6 = \underline{13}$

22. **THINK SMARTER** Sam painted 3 pictures. Ellie painted twice as many pictures as Sam. How many pictures did they paint altogether?

$\underline{9}$ pictures

PROBLEM TYPE SITUATIONS

Addition and Subtraction

Add To • Result Unknown
Exercise: 25

Put Together/Take Apart • Total Unknown
Exercises: 22, 23, 24

Problem Solving • Applications (Real World)

WRITE ▸ Math

Solve. Write or draw to explain.

23. **GO DEEPER** Chloe draws 8 pictures. Reggie draws 1 more picture than Chloe. How many pictures do they draw?

_____17_____ pictures

24. **MATHEMATICAL PRACTICE ①** Analyze Joanne made 9 clay bowls last week. She made the same number of clay bowls this week. How many clay bowls did she make in two weeks?

_____18_____ clay bowls

25. **THINK SMARTER +** There are 9 raisins in the bowl. Devon puts 8 more raisins in the bowl. Complete the addition sentence to find how many raisins are in the bowl now.

Personal Math Trainer

_____9_____ + _____8_____ = _____17_____   Also accept 8 + 9 = 17.

_____17_____ raisins

 TAKE HOME ACTIVITY • Ask your child to write several addition facts that he or she knows.

172 one hundred seventy-two

© Houghton Mifflin Harcourt Publishing Company

Problem Solving • Applications (Real World)

Common Core MATHEMATICAL PRACTICES

MP1 Make sense of problems and persevere in solving them. Have children read Exercise 23. Ask them to describe how they will solve the problem.

THINK SMARTER +
Personal Math Trainer

Be sure to assign this exercise to students in the Personal Math Trainer. It features an animation to help them model and answer the exercise. Exercise 25 is a non-routine, multistep problem. Have children describe all the steps they will use to solve. Children may be able to translate the problem situation into an equation and correctly complete the left side of the equation. If children do not find the correct sum, they may have difficulty recalling addition facts.

⑤ EVALUATE Formative Assessment

Essential Question

Reflect Using the Language Objective Have children recommend to a partner two ways to answer the Essential Question.

What are some ways to remember sums?

Possible answer: I can count on by 1, 2, or 3; change the order of the addends; or use doubles facts. I also know that any number plus 0 equals that number.

Math Journal WRITE ▸ Math

Write or draw to explain a way to find each sum: 6 + 7, 8 + 4, 2 + 9.

 DIFFERENTIATED INSTRUCTION **INDEPENDENT ACTIVITIES**

Grab and Go!™
Differentiated Centers Kit

Activities	**Literature**	**Games**
Ring Toss	**Doubles Fun on the Farm**	**Caterpillar Chase**

Games

Children complete orange Activity Card 1 by adding numbers to 18.

Children read the book and add equal groups to make doubles.

Children practice basic addition facts to move along the game path.

Practice and Homework

Use the Practice and Homework pages to provide children with more practice of the concepts and skills presented in this lesson. Children master their understanding as they complete practice items and then challenge their critical thinking skills with Problem Solving. Use the Write Math section to determine children's understanding of content for this lesson. Encourage children to use their Math Journals to record their answers.

Name _____

Practice Addition Facts

Common Core **COMMON CORE STANDARD—2.OA.B.2**
Add and subtract within 20.

Write the sums.

1. 9 + 1 = __10__

    1 + 9 = __10__

2. 7 + 6 = __13__

    6 + 7 = __13__

3. 8 + 0 = __8__

    5 + 0 = __5__

4. __16__ = 7 + 9

    __16__ = 9 + 7

5. 4 + 4 = __8__

    4 + 5 = __9__

6. 9 + 9 = __18__

    9 + 8 = __17__

7. 8 + 8 = __16__

    8 + 7 = __15__

8. 2 + 2 = __4__

    2 + 3 = __5__

9. __9__ = 6 + 3

    __9__ = 3 + 6

10. 6 + 6 = __12__

    6 + 7 = __13__

11. __7__ = 0 + 7

    __9__ = 0 + 9

12. 5 + 5 = __10__

    5 + 6 = __11__

Problem Solving (Real World)

Solve. Write or draw to explain.

13. Jason has 7 puzzles. Quincy has the same number of puzzles as Jason. How many puzzles do they have altogether?

    __14__ puzzles

14. **WRITE** Math Write or draw to explain a way to find each sum: 6 + 7, 8 + 4, 2 + 9.

    _____

    Check children's work.

Chapter 3

one hundred seventy-three **173**

Cross-Curricular S.T.E.M.

- Discuss with children the properties of flowering plants, including color. As the children name the colors of various flowering plants, write this information on the board.

- Have children write addition sentences to show various combinations of flowers. For example, for the flowers above, they might write 4 + 5 = 9.
- Have children explain a strategy they can use to find the sum.

SOCIAL STUDIES

Materials calendar

- Discuss the calendar with children. Review how to identify the days of the week and the dates for those days. Ask questions such as "How many Mondays are in the month?"
- Have children solve this problem. **Mimi plays soccer every Tuesday and Friday. How many times does she play this month?**
- Have children count the number of Tuesdays and the number of Fridays in the current month. Then have them write a number sentence for the problem and solve.

October

Sunday	Monday	Tuesday	Wednesday	Thursday	Friday	Saturday
						1
2	3	4	5	6	7	8
9	10	11	12	13	14	15
16	17	18	19	20	21	22
23	24	25	26	27	28	29
30	31					

1. What is the sum?

    $8 + 7 = \underline{15}$

2. What is the sum?

    $2 + 9 = \underline{11}$

Spiral Review (2.NBT.A.2, 2.NBT.A.3, 2.NBT.A.4, 2.NBT.B.8)

3. Write another way to describe 43.

    Possible answer:

    $\underline{40} + \underline{3}$

4. Write the number that is 100 more than 276.

    $\underline{376}$

5. Count by tens.

    20, 30, 40, $\underline{50}$, $\underline{60}$, $\underline{70}$

6. Write <, >, or = to compare.

    127 $\underline{<}$ 142

FOR MORE PRACTICE
GO TO THE
Personal Math Trainer

Continue concepts and skills practice with Lesson Check. Use Spiral Review to engage children in previously taught concepts and to promote content retention. Common Core standards are correlated to each section.

Algebra • Make a Ten to Add

LESSON AT A GLANCE

F C R Focus:

Common Core State Standards

2.OA.B.2 Fluently add and subtract within 20 using mental strategies. By end of Grade 2, know from memory all sums of two one-digit numbers.

MATHEMATICAL PRACTICES (See *Mathematical Practices in GO Math!* in the *Planning Guide* for full text.)
MP1 Make sense of problems and persevere in solving them. **MP5** Use appropriate tools strategically. **MP6** Attend to precision. **MP7** Look for and make use of structure. **MP8** Look for and express regularity in repeated reasoning.

F C R Coherence:

Standards Across the Grades

Before	Grade 2	After
1.OA.A.1	2.OA.B.2	3.OA.D.8
1.OA.C.6		

F C R Rigor:

Level 1: Understand Concepts....................*Share and Show* (✓ Checked Items)
Level 2: Procedural Skills and Fluency.......*On Your Own, Practice and Homework*
Level 3: Applications...................................*Think Smarter and Go Deeper*

Learning Objective

Recall sums for addition facts using the make a ten strategy.

Language Objective

Children demonstrate the *make a ten* strategy and tell how it is used to find sums.

Materials

MathBoard

F C R For more about how *GO Math!* fosters **Coherence** within the Content Standards and Mathematical Progressions for this chapter, see page 159J.

About the Math

Professional Development

Progress to Algebra
Using a Ten Frame

A ten frame is a spatial organizer for children. It may be used to develop mental images or representations for combinations of numbers that have a sum of 10.

Introduce the ten frame using a realistic example. For example, tell children there are ten cubbies on a shelf. Six of the cubbies are filled with one backpack each. Show six red counters in a ten frame.

Ask children how many more backpacks are needed to fill the rest of the cubbies. Move yellow counters into the four empty spaces to show children that four backpacks are needed to fill the remaining cubbies.

Working with ten frames will help children recall pairs of numbers that have a sum of 10, an important skill used in addition and subtraction computation with greater numbers. You may want to use the pages with ten frames (with dots pictured) in the *eTeacher Resources* as flashcards for extra practice and games.

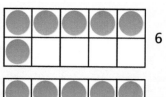
6 + ___ = 10

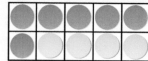
6 + 4 = 10

 Professional Development Videos

Problem of the Day 3.3

Number of the Day 327

Show the number in several different ways.
Check children's work.

Have children discuss the different ways they can represent the number. For example, they might draw a quick picture or use base-ten blocks.

Vocabulary

GO DIGITAL
• Interactive Student Edition
• Multimedia *eGlossary*

Fluency Task

Read these expressions aloud to students. Ask them to raise their hands each time you say an addition expression that adds to 10.

- **4 + 4**
- **6 + 4**
- **5 + 5**
- **2 + 9**
- **7 + 3**
- **2 + 8**
- **5 + 4**
- **9 + 1**
- **8 + 3**

➊ ENGAGE

with the Interactive Student Edition

Essential Question
How is the *make a ten* strategy used to find sums?

Making Connections
Assess prior knowledge. Review breaking apart numbers.

What does it mean to break something apart? Answers will vary. **How do you break apart numbers?** Answers will vary. **What are some ways that you can break apart 5? 10?** 0 + 5, 1 + 4, 2 + 3, 3 + 2, 4 + 1, 5 + 0, 0 + 10, 1 + 9, 2 + 8, etc.

Learning Activity
What is the problem the children are trying to solve? Guide the children to think about making tens.

- **How many lily pads did Jessie see at first?** 9
- **How many did Jessie see next?** 4
- **What does Jessie want to find?** the total number of lily pads
- **What might you do to help Jessie add the lily pads?** Answers will vary.

Literacy and Mathematics
View the lesson opener with the children. Then, choose one or more of the following activities.

- Ask children to write sentences about a group of things that is broken apart.
- Help the children act out a story about groups of friends that come together by first making a group of ten.

② EXPLORE

Listen and Draw MATHEMATICAL PRACTICES

MP7 Look for and make use of structure. Read the following problem.

There are 6 large dogs and 4 small dogs. How many dogs are there?

Have children point to the ten frame that is a model for the problem. Ask children to write the addition sentence for the model.
6 + 4 = 10

- **What if there were 5 large dogs and 5 small dogs? Point to the ten frame. Write an addition sentence for this model.**
5 + 5 = 10

- **Point to the ten frame that is a model for 8 large dogs and 2 small dogs. Write an addition sentence for this model.** 8 + 2 = 10

- **What if there were 9 large dogs and 1 small dog? Write an addition sentence for this model.** 9 + 1 = 10

- **Which is a model for 7 large dogs and 3 small dogs? Write an addition sentence for this model.** 7 + 3 = 10

- **How are these facts alike?** They all have a sum of 10. **How are they different?** They have different addends.

 MP7 Look for and make use of structure. Use **Math Talk** to focus on children's understanding of the *make a ten* strategy.

ELL **Strategy:**
Model Concepts

Children may understand the make a ten strategy when it is modeled.

- Place 9 counters in the ten frame. Explain that 1 more counter is needed to make 10.

- Discuss how to make 10 in different ways.

- Guide children in using the counters in the ten frame to make 10. Have children write the number sentence for each way they make 10.

175 Chapter 3

Progress to Algebra

2.OA.B.2 Fluently add and subtract within 20 using mental strategies. By end of Grade 2, know from memory all sums of two one-digit numbers.

Name _____

Lesson 3.3

Algebra • Make a Ten to Add

Essential Question How is the make a ten strategy used to find sums?

Common Core Operations and Algebraic Thinking—2.OA.B.2
MATHEMATICAL PRACTICES
MP1, MP7, MP8

Problem Type:
Put Together/Take Apart •
Total Unknown

Listen and Draw

Write the fact below the ten frame when you hear the problem that matches the model.

5 + 5 = 10

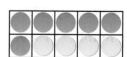

6 + 4 = 10

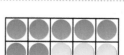

7 + 3 = 10

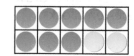

8 + 2 = 10

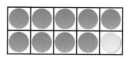

9 + 1 = 10

Math Talk: Some possible patterns: the sums are all 10; as the first addend increases by 1, the second addend decreases by 1.

 FOR THE TEACHER • Read the following problem. There are 6 large dogs and 4 small dogs. How many dogs are there? Have children find the ten frame that models the problem and write the addition sentence. Repeat by revising the story for each addition fact represented by the other ten frames.

Math Talk MATHEMATICAL PRACTICES 7

Look for Structure Describe a pattern you see in these make a ten facts.

Chapter 3

one hundred seventy-five **175**

Reteach 3.3 ▲ RtI

Name _____
Lesson 3.3
Reteach

Algebra • Make a Ten to Add

8 + 5 = __?__

Step ① Start with the greater addend.

8   +   5

Step ② Break apart the other addend to make a ten.
You need to add 2 to 8 to make a ten. So, break apart 5 as 2 and 3.

8 + 2 = 10   3

Step ③ Add 3 to find the sum.   10 + __3__ = __13__

Step ④ Write the sum.   8 + 5 = __13__

Show how you can make a ten to find the sum. Write the sum.

1. 7 + 6 = __13__
    3   3
    10 + __3__ = __13__

2. 9 + 2 = __11__
    1   1
    10 + __1__ = __11__

3. 4 + 8 = __12__
    2   2
    10 + __2__ = __12__

4. 5 + 9 = __14__
    10 + __4__ = __14__

5. 8 + 6 = __14__
    10 + __4__ = __14__

6. 4 + 9 = __13__
    10 + __3__ = __13__

Chapter Resources
© Houghton Mifflin Harcourt Publishing Company
3-9
Reteach

Enrich 3.3 **Differentiated Instruction**

Name _____
Lesson 3.3
Enrich

Make a Ten Again

Write the fact. Circle ten animals. Then write the make a ten fact to find the total number of animals.

__8__ + __5__ = ?
__10__ + __3__ = __13__

__9__ + __5__ = ?
__10__ + __4__ = __14__

__8__ + __8__ = ?
__10__ + __6__ = __16__

__5__ + __7__ = ?
__10__ + __2__ = __12__

Writing and Reasoning How did you decide which make a ten fact to use? Explain.
Possible answer: After I circled each group of ten, I looked at the number of animals left. Then I added that number to 10.

Chapter Resources
© Houghton Mifflin Harcourt Publishing Company
3-10
Enrich

Model and Draw

7 + 5 = ?

You need to add 3 to 7 to make a ten. Break apart 5 as 3 and 2.

$7 + 5$

$7 + 3 + 2$

$10 + 2 = \underline{\ 12\ }$

So, $7 + 5 = \underline{\ 12\ }$.

Share and Show

Show how you can make a ten to find the sum. Write the sum.

1. $8 + 3 = \underline{\ 11\ }$

$10 + \underline{\ 1\ } = \underline{\ 11\ }$

2. $2 + 9 = \underline{\ 11\ }$

$10 + \underline{\ 1\ } = \underline{\ 11\ }$

3. $8 + 5 = \underline{\ 13\ }$

$10 + \underline{\ 3\ } = \underline{\ 13\ }$

4. $4 + 7 = \underline{\ 11\ }$

$10 + \underline{\ 1\ } = \underline{\ 11\ }$

5. $3 + 9 = \underline{\ 12\ }$

$10 + \underline{\ 2\ } = \underline{\ 12\ }$

6. $7 + 6 = \underline{\ 13\ }$

$10 + \underline{\ 3\ } = \underline{\ 13\ }$

176 one hundred seventy-six

© Houghton Mifflin Harcourt Publishing Company

Model and Draw

MP6 Attend to precision. Work through the model with children.

- **Why is 5 broken apart as 3 and 2 to solve?**
  Possible answer: A 3 is needed to make a ten with 7.
- **Why is 10 + 2 the last step in the cloud?**
  Possible answer: 5 was broken apart as 3 and 2. The 3 was added to 7 to make 10, so the 2 still needs to be added to find the sum.

Be sure children realize this strategy makes sense only when the sum is 10 or greater.

EXPLAIN

Share and Show

Connect Exercises 1–6 to the learning model.

- **Do you think it is easier to break apart the greater addend or the lesser addend? Explain.** Possible answer: the lesser addend; It is easier to look at the greater addend and decide how to break apart the other addend to make a 10.

Use the checked exercises for **Quick Check.** Children should use their Math Boards to show their solutions to these exercises.

✓ Quick Check RtI

If ▶ a child misses the checked exercises

Then ▶ **Differentiate Instruction** with
- Reteach 3.3
- Personal Math trainer 2.OA.B.2
- RtI Tier 1 Activity (online)

⚠ COMMON ERRORS

Error Children may break apart the addend into a combination that does not make a ten, and then continue on as if it did make a ten.

Example $7 + 8 = $

$4 \quad 4$

$10 + 4 = 14$

Springboard to Learning Have children use a ten frame to help them remember facts with sums of 10.

Lesson 3.3 **176**

On Your Own

If a child answers the checked exercises correctly, assign Exercises 7–14.

 THINK SMARTER

In Exercise 14, children use higher order thinking skills as they find a missing addend in an addition word problem. In this problem, the amount of change (how many more bees need to go in the hive) is the unknown. Encourage children to use the *make a ten* strategy to find the missing addend.

• **How can you use the *make a ten* strategy to help you find the missing addend in Exercise 15?** Possible answer: The known addend is 5. The missing addend is the addend that will be broken apart. I know 5 + 5 = 10, so one part of the missing addend is 5. The other part of the missing addend is 4, because 14 = 10 + 4. To find the missing addend I add 5 and 4.

 Math on the Spot Video Tutor
Use this video to help children model and solve this type of *Think Smarter* problem.

GO DIGITAL Math on the Spot videos are in the Interactive Student Edition and at *www.thinkcentral.com*.

GO DEEPER

MP5 Use appropriate tools strategically. Explain to children that the *make a ten* strategy is most effective when making ten with the greater addend.

Some children may find it easier to always break apart the second addend in an addition sentence. Discuss with children how changing the order of addends does not change the sum. They can rewrite an addition sentence so that the greater addend is the first addend and the addend that they need to break apart is the second addend.

Name _____

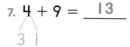

On Your Own

Show how you can make a ten to find the sum. Write the sum.

7. $4 + 9 =$ ___13___
   3 | 1

   $10 +$ ___3___ $=$ ___13___

8. $9 + 8 =$ ___17___
   1 | 7

   $10 +$ ___7___ $=$ ___17___

9. $8 + 6 =$ ___14___

   $10 +$ ___4___ $=$ ___14___

10. $5 + 9 =$ ___14___

   $10 +$ ___4___ $=$ ___14___

11. $7 + 9 =$ ___16___

   $10 +$ ___6___ $=$ ___16___

12. $8 + 4 =$ ___12___

   $10 +$ ___2___ $=$ ___12___

13. **GO DEEPER** Alex is thinking of a doubles fact. The sum is greater than the sum of 7 + 7 but less than the sum of 8 + 9. What fact is Alex thinking of?

   ___8___ $+$ ___8___ $=$ ___16___

14. **THINK** SMARTER There were 5 bees in a hive. How many more bees need to go in the hive for there to be 14 bees?

   ___9___ more bees

PROBLEM TYPE SITUATIONS

Addition and Subtraction

Put Together/Take Apart • Total Unknown
Exercises: 15, 17

Compare • Bigger Unknown
Exercise: 14

Problem Solving • Applications | WRITE ▸ Math

Solve. Write or draw to explain.

15. **MATHEMATICAL PRACTICE ①** Analyze There are 9 large bicycles at the store. There are 6 small bicycles at the store. How many bicycles are at the store?

_____15_____ bicycles

16. **GO DEEPER** Max is thinking of a doubles fact. It has a sum that is greater than the sum of 6 + 4 but less than the sum of 8 + 5. What fact is Max thinking of?

___6___ + ___6___ = ___12___

17. **THINK SMARTER** Natasha had 8 shells. Then she found 5 more shells. Draw to show how to find the number of shells Natasha has now.

Check children's drawing.

How many shells does she have now?   ___13___ shells

 TAKE HOME ACTIVITY • Ask your child to name pairs of numbers that have a sum of 10. Then have him or her write the addition sentences.

178 one hundred seventy-eight

© Houghton Mifflin Harcourt Publishing Company • Image Credits: (b) ©Siede Preis/Photodisc/Getty Images

---

DIFFERENTIATED INSTRUCTION | **INDEPENDENT ACTIVITIES**

Differentiated Centers Kit

Activities
Ring Toss

 Children complete orange Activity Card 1 by adding numbers to 18.

Games
Caterpillar Chase

 Children practice basic addition facts to move along the game path.

Problem Solving • Applications

MATHEMATICAL PRACTICES

MP1 Make sense of problems and persevere in solving them. Have children read Exercise 15. Ask them to describe how they will solve the problem. Children may use the *make a ten* strategy.

GO DEEPER

To solve Exercise 16, children use clues to find a doubles fact.

- **What do you know about the sum of this doubles fact?** It is between 10 and 13.

THINK SMARTER

Students will be able to draw a correct model if they understand how to use the strategy *make a ten*. Students might get the number of shells correct, but make an incorrect model if they recognize this as an addition problem and recall the addition fact, but do not understand how to represent the strategy using a drawing.

5 EVALUATE Formative Assessment

Essential Question

Reflect Using the Language Objective Have children demonstrate and explain the make a ten strategy to answer the Essential Question.

How is the *make a ten* strategy used to find sums? Possible answer: You break apart the lesser addend to make a ten. You add 10 plus the remaining part of the addend to find the sum.

Math Journal  WRITE ▸ Math

Describe how you can use the make a ten strategy to find the sum of 7 + 9.

Practice and Homework

Use the Practice and Homework pages to provide children with more practice of the concepts and skills presented in this lesson. Children master their understanding as they complete practice items and then challenge their critical thinking skills with Problem Solving. Use the Write Math section to determine children's understanding of content for this lesson. Encourage children to use their Math Journals to record their answers.

Algebra • Make a Ten to Add

Common Core COMMON CORE STANDARD—2.OA.B.2
Add and subtract within 20.

Show how you can make a ten to find the sum. Write the sum.

1. $9 + 7 = \underline{16}$

   $10 + \underline{6} = \underline{16}$

2. $8 + 5 = \underline{13}$

   $10 + \underline{3} = \underline{13}$

3. $8 + 6 = \underline{14}$

   $10 + \underline{4} = \underline{14}$

4. $3 + 9 = \underline{12}$

   $10 + \underline{2} = \underline{12}$

5. $8 + 7 = \underline{15}$

   $10 + \underline{5} = \underline{15}$

6. $6 + 5 = \underline{11}$

   $10 + \underline{1} = \underline{11}$

Problem Solving (Real World)

Solve. Write or draw to explain.

7. There are 9 children on the bus. Then 8 more children get on the bus. How many children are on the bus now?

   $\underline{17}$ children

8. **WRITE Math** Describe how you can use the make a ten strategy to find the sum $7 + 9$.

   _____

   Check children's work.

© Houghton Mifflin Harcourt Publishing Company

Lesson Check (2.OA.B.2)

1. Circle the fact with the same sum as 8 + 7.

   10 + 3

   10 + 4

   (10 + 5)

   10 + 6

2. Write a fact with the same sum as 7 + 5.

   Possible answer:

   _10_ + _2_

Spiral Review (2.OA.C.3, 2.NBT.A.3)

3. Write the number shown by 200 + 10 + 7.

   217

4. Circle the odd number.

   2   4   6   (7)

5. What is the value of the underlined digit?

   6̲5

   60

6. What is another way to write the number 47?

   Possible answer:

   _4_ tens _7_ ones

FOR MORE PRACTICE
GO TO THE
Personal Math Trainer

Continue concepts and skills practice with Lesson Check. Use Spiral Review to engage children in previously taught concepts and to promote content retention. Common Core standards are correlated to each section.

Algebra • Add 3 Addends

LESSON AT A GLANCE

FOCUS   COHERENCE   RIGOR

F C R Focus:

Common Core State Standards

2.OA.B.2 Fluently add and subtract within 20 using mental strategies. By end of Grade 2, know from memory all sums of two one-digit numbers.

2.NBT.B.5 Fluently add and subtract within 100 using strategies based on place value, properties of operations, and/or the relationship between addition and subtraction.

MATHEMATICAL PRACTICES (See *Mathematical Practices in GO Math!* in the *Planning Guide* for full text.)
MP1 Make sense of problems and persevere in solving them. **MP6** Attend to precision. **MP7** Look for and make use of structure. **MP8** Look for and express regularity in repeated reasoning.

F C R Coherence:

Standards Across the Grades

Before	Grade 2	After
1.OA.A.1	2.OA.B.2	3.OA.D.8
1.OA.C.6		

F C R Rigor:

Level 1: Understand Concepts....................*Share and Show* (✓ Checked Items)
Level 2: Procedural Skills and Fluency.......*On Your Own, Practice and Homework*
Level 3: Applications..................................*Think Smarter and Go Deeper*

Learning Objective

Find sums of three addends by applying the Commutative and Associative Properties of Addition.

Language Objective

Children complete the sentence frame, **When you add three numbers, first you add _____, next you add ____ and finally you _____.**

Materials

MathBoard

F C R For more about how *GO Math!* fosters **Coherence** within the Content Standards and Mathematical Progressions for this chapter, see page 159J..

About the Math

Professional Development

Progress to Algebra
Why Teach This?

In this chapter, children use two important addition properties.

- In Lesson 3.2 they learned that changing the order of the addends does not change the sum. This is the Commutative Property of Addition. Understanding this property helps children build fluency by reducing the number of facts they need to memorize.

- In this lesson, children learn that changing the way addends are grouped does not change the sum. This is known as the Associative Property of Addition. Understanding that when adding 3 + 2 + 6, you first can add 3 + 2, or 3 + 6, or 2 + 6 and then add the third addend to that sum, gives children the option of finding the sum by using facts they know and the strategies that work best for them.

 Professional Development Videos

 GO DIGITAL

SE Interactive Student Edition

Personal Math Trainer

Math on the Spot Video

Animated Math Models

*i*T *i*Tools: Counters

HMH Mega Math

Daily Routines

Common Core

 Problem of the Day 3.4

Number of the Day 381

- **What number is 1 hundred less?** 281
- **What number is 1 ten less?** 371
- **What number is 1 one less?** 380

Vocabulary

GO DIGITAL
- Interactive Student Edition
- Multimedia eGlossary

Fluency Builder

Have children practice these doubles facts, then have them add 1 to the sum.

- **4 + 4; then add 1**
- **2 + 2; then add 1**
- **7 + 7; then add 1**
- **3 + 3; then add 1**
- **5 + 5; then add 1**
- **8 + 8; then add 1**
- **6 + 6; then add 1**

① ENGAGE

with the Interactive Student Edition

Essential Question

How do you add three numbers?

Making Connections

Ask children what they know about adding numbers.

What are some addition facts you have learned so far? Check children's work. **Do the addition facts 8 + 2 and 2 + 8 have the same sum?** Yes. **Can you always add addends in any order? Explain.** Check children's explanations.

Learning Activity

What is the problem the children are trying to solve? Connect the story to the problem. Ask the following questions.

- **How is adding more than two addends like skip counting by 2s or 5s?** Sample answer: skip counting by 2s is the same as 2, 2 + 2, 2 + 2 + 2, etc. Skip counting by 5s is alike in the same way.

Literacy and Mathematics

View the lesson opener with the children. Then, choose one or more of the following activities:

- Have children write a story about adding two or more addends. Have them draw a square around each addend.
- Have children represent three numbers less than 10 with connecting cubes and then join them to find the total.

② EXPLORE

Listen and Draw Common Core MATHEMATICAL PRACTICES

MP6 Attend to precision. Read the directions aloud with children. After children have recorded the sum of each pair of addends, have them share their answers and discuss the strategies used.

- **Were there sums that you found more quickly than others? Explain.** Possible answer: I found the sum of 1 and 4 quickly because I know that 5 is one more than 4.

- **Which sums did you find by using a doubles fact?** Possible answer: I used a doubles fact to find the sums of 3 + 3 and 5 + 4.

- **Name a different fact that has a sum of 8.** Possible answers: 0 + 8 = 8; 1 + 7 = 8; 3 + 5 = 8; 4 + 4 = 8

Math Talk **MP1 Make sense of problems and persevere in solving them.** Use Math Talk to focus on children's understanding of different strategies they can use to add.

ELL Strategy:
Model Concepts

Children may understand concepts, story problems, and vocabulary if they are illustrated or modeled.

- **Write this problem on the board and then read it aloud.**

  Peter has 4 books. Carla has 6 books. Manuela has 3 books. How many books do they have in all?

- **Have children model the problem using addition fact cards and then discuss different ways they can use the cards to solve the problem.** 13 books

181 Chapter 3

Progress to Algebra

2.OA.B.2 Fluently add and subtract within 20 using mental strategies. By end of Grade 2, know from memory all sums of two one-digit numbers.
2.NBT.B.5 Fluently add and subtract within 100 using strategies based on place value, properties of operations, and/or the relationship between addition and subtraction.

Name _____

Lesson 3.4

Algebra • Add 3 Addends
Essential Question How do you add three numbers?

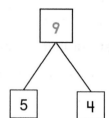 Common Core **Operations and Algebraic Thinking—2.OA.B.2** Also 2.NBT.B.5
MATHEMATICAL PRACTICES
MP1, MP7, MP8

Listen and Draw

Write the sum of each pair of addends.

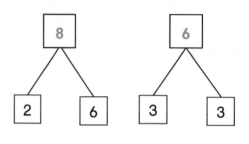

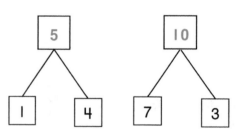

Math Talk: Possible answer: I know that 5 + 5 = 10, so I subtracted 1 to get 9.

 **FOR THE TEACHER •** After children have recorded the sum of each pair of addends, have them share their answers and discuss the strategies used.

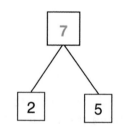 **Math Talk** MATHEMATICAL PRACTICES

Describe how you found the sum of 5 and 4.

Chapter 3

one hundred eighty-one **181**

Reteach 3.4 ▲RtI

Lesson 3.4 Reteach

Name _____

Algebra • Add 3 Addends

Add numbers in any order.
The sum stays the same.

1 + 4 + 6 = 11   1 + 4 + 6 = 11   1 + 4 + 6 = 11
5 + 6 = 11   1 + 10 = 11   7 + 4 = 11

Solve two ways. Circle the two addends you add first.
Circled addends will vary.

1. 2 + 3 + 2 = __7__   2 + 3 + 2 = __7__

2. 7 + 2 + 3 = __12__   7 + 2 + 3 = __12__

3. 1 + 1 + 9 = __11__   1 + 1 + 9 = __11__

4. 6 + 4 + 4 = __14__   6 + 4 + 4 = __14__

Chapter Resources   3-11   Reteach
© Houghton Mifflin Harcourt Publishing Company

Enrich 3.4 **Differentiated Instruction**

Lesson 3.4 Enrich

Name _____

Finding Sums

Use two sets of cards for numbers 0–9.
Play with a classmate.
Take three cards to get three addends.
Write the sum.
Answers will vary. Check children's work.

	1st Card	2nd Card	3rd Card	Sum
1.				
2.				
3.				
4.				
5.				

Writing and Reasoning Explain how you decided which two numbers to add first for one of your sums.

Possible answer: First, I looked for numbers to make a ten. Then, I added the third number to the 10. If there was not a way to make a ten, I looked for other facts that I know.

Chapter Resources   3-12   Enrich
© Houghton Mifflin Harcourt Publishing Company

Model and Draw

You can group numbers in different ways to add.

Choose two addends.
Look for facts you know.

Changing the way the numbers are grouped does not change the sum.

$3 + 2 + 7 = ?$
$5 + 7 = \underline{12}$

$3 + 2 + 7 = ?$
$3 + 9 = \underline{12}$

$3 + 2 + 7 = ?$
$10 + 2 = \underline{12}$

Share and Show

Solve two ways. Circle the two addends you add first.
Circled addends will vary.

1. $1 + 8 + 2 = \underline{11}$ $1 + 8 + 2 = \underline{11}$

2. $7 + 3 + 3 = \underline{13}$ $7 + 3 + 3 = \underline{13}$

3. $4 + 2 + 4 = \underline{10}$ $4 + 2 + 4 = \underline{10}$

4. $2 + 8 + 2 = \underline{12}$ $2 + 8 + 2 = \underline{12}$

5.
```
   3        3
   2        2
 + 6      + 6
----     ----
  11       11
```

6.
```
   7        7
   0        0
 + 2      + 2
----     ----
   9        9
```

182 one hundred eighty-two

Advanced Learners
Visual / Linguistic
Individual / Partners

Materials three sets of Numeral Cards 1–9 (see *eTeacher Resources*)

- Shuffle the numeral cards and place them facedown. Have each child take three cards and add the numbers.

- The child with the greater total gets one point. The first child to get 10 points wins.

- Have partners check each other's work and discuss how they grouped the numbers to add. Have them repeat the activity with other numbers.

$7 + 8 + 2 = 17$ $5 + 3 + 6 = 14$

Model and Draw  MATHEMATICAL PRACTICES

Work through the model with children.

- **What is different about the three ways?**
  Different numbers are grouped together in the first step of solving the problem. **What is the same?**
  The sum is the same.

③ EXPLAIN

Share and Show

Connect Exercises 1–6 to the learning model.

- **In Exercise 1, which addends did you group first for the two different ways?**
  Possible answer: For the first way, I grouped 1 and 8 and got 9, and then I added on 2 for a sum of 11. For the second way, I grouped 8 and 2 and got 10 and then added on 1 for a sum of 11.

- **How does solving in two ways help you know that your answer is correct?** Possible answer: If I get the same sum both ways, then my answer is probably correct.

Use the checked exercises for **Quick Check**. Children should use their MathBoards to show their solutions to these exercises.

Quick Check   RtI

If	a child misses the checked exercises
Then	**Differentiate Instruction** with

- Reteach 3.4
- Personal Math trainer 2.OA.B.2, 2.NBT.B.5
- RtI Tier 1 Activity (online)

! COMMON ERRORS

Error Children may find the sum for two addends and forget to add the third addend.

Example $2 + 8 + 2 = 10$

Springboard to Learning After children circle the two addends they add first, have them write the sum of these addends below the problem. Encourage them to draw arrows pointing from this sum to the two addends. Then they can see that they need to add the third addend to the sum they wrote.

Lesson 3.4   182

④ ELABORATE

On Your Own

If a child answers the checked exercises correctly, assign Exercises 7–18.

Ask a volunteer to describe two ways to group the addends in the expression 5 + 1 + 4.

- **Do you start with 5 and count on 1? Or do you add 1 + 4 and then find the sum of 5 + 5? Is there another way to find the sum?** Children's answers should demonstrate understanding that changing the way addends are grouped does not change the sum.

MP7 Look for and make use of structure.
For Exercises 15–18, children use higher order thinking skills as they find a missing addend for an addition problem that is written in vertical format. Point out to children that the phrases "missing addend" and "unknown addend" mean the same thing.

- **How did you find the missing addend in Exercise 15?** Possible answer: First I found the sum of 5 + 5, which is 10. Then I thought "10 plus what number is 14?" 10 + 4 = 14, so the missing addend is 4.

 Go DEEPER

Write the following problem on the board.

$$5 + \underline{\hphantom{00}} + \underline{\hphantom{00}} = 11$$

Challenge children to complete the addition sentence in as many ways as they can. Record their answers on the board. Then discuss patterns they see in the problems.

5 + 0 + 6 = 11
5 + 1 + 5 = 11
5 + 2 + 4 = 11
5 + 3 + 3 = 11
5 + 4 + 2 = 11
5 + 5 + 1 = 11
5 + 6 + 0 = 11

Name _____

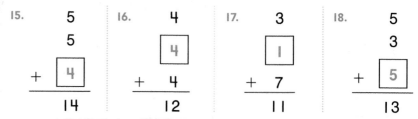 **On Your Own**

Solve two ways. Circle the two addends you add first.

Circled addends will vary.

7. 4 + 1 + 6 = __11__   4 + 1 + 6 = __11__

8. 4 + 3 + 3 = __10__   4 + 3 + 3 = __10__

9. 1 + 5 + 3 = __9__   1 + 5 + 3 = __9__

10. 6 + 4 + 4 = __14__   6 + 4 + 4 = __14__

11. 5 + 5 + 5 = __15__   5 + 5 + 5 = __15__

12. 7 + 0 + 6 = __13__   7 + 0 + 6 = __13__

13.
```
    5        5
    3        3
  + 4      + 4
  ────     ────
   12       12
```

14.
```
    4        4
    2        2
  + 5      + 5
  ────     ────
   11       11
```

MATHEMATICAL PRACTICE ⑦ Look for Structure

Write the missing addend.

15.
```
    5
    5
  + ☐4
  ────
   14
```

16.
```
    4
   ☐4
  + 4
  ────
   12
```

17.
```
    3
   ☐1
  + 7
  ────
   11
```

18.
```
    5
    3
  + ☐5
  ────
   13
```

© Houghton Mifflin Harcourt Publishing Company

Chapter 3 • Lesson 4   one hundred eighty-three **183**

PROBLEM TYPE SITUATIONS

Addition and Subtraction

Add To • Result Unknown
Exercise: 20

Add To • Change Unknown
Exercise: 19

Put Together/Take Apart • Total Unknown
Exercises: 19, 20, 21

Problem Solving • Applications (Real World) WRITE ▶ Math

Choose a way to solve.
Write or draw to explain.

19. *THINK SMARTER* Nick, Alex, and
Sophia eat 15 raisins in all.
Nick and Alex each eat
4 raisins. How many raisins
does Sophia eat?

_____7_____ raisins

20. MATHEMATICAL PRACTICE ① **Analyze**
There are 5 green grapes
and 4 red grapes in a bowl.
Eli puts 4 more grapes in
the bowl. How many grapes
are in the bowl now?

_____13_____ grapes

21. *THINK SMARTER* Mrs. Moore bought
4 small apples, 6 medium apples,
and 3 large apples. How many
apples did she buy?

_____13_____ apples

 TAKE HOME ACTIVITY • Have your child describe
two ways to add 3, 6, and 2.

184 one hundred eighty-four

Problem Solving • Applications (Real World)
Common Core **MATHEMATICAL PRACTICES**

THINK SMARTER

For Exercise 19, children find a missing
addend in an addition word problem. Have
children explain how they got their answers.
Guide a discussion about the different ways
children chose to solve the problem.

**Math on the Spot
Video Tutor**
Use this video to help children model and solve
this type of *Think Smarter* problem.

GO DIGITAL **Math on the Spot** videos are in the Interactive
Student Edition and at *www.thinkcentral.com.*

**MP1 Make sense of problems and
persevere in solving them.** Have children
read Exercise 20. Ask them to describe how
they will solve the problem. A key to solving
Exercise 20 is realizing that it is an addition
problem with three addends.

THINK SMARTER

In Exercise 21, children may not include all
of the addends in the total sum. Incorrect
sums that would indicate children omitted an
addend are 7, 9, and 10.

⑤ EVALUATE Formative Assessment

Essential Question

Reflect **Using the Language Objective** Have
children complete the sentence frame, When
you add three numbers, first you add _____,
next you add ____ and finally you _____, to
answer the Essential Question.

How do you add three numbers? Possible
answer: You add any two addends first and then add the
third addend to that sum.

Math Journal WRITE ▶ Math

Write or draw to explain two ways you can
find the sum of 3 + 4 + 5.

DIFFERENTIATED INSTRUCTION INDEPENDENT ACTIVITIES

Differentiated Centers Kit

**Activities
Ring Toss**

 Children
complete
orange
Activity Card
1 by adding
numbers to 18.

**Games
Caterpillar Chase**

 Children
practice basic
addition facts to
move along the
game path.

Practice and Homework

Use the Practice and Homework pages to provide children with more practice of the concepts and skills presented in this lesson. Children master their understanding as they complete practice items and then challenge their critical thinking skills with Problem Solving. Use the Write Math section to determine children's understanding of content for this lesson. Encourage children to use their Math Journals to record their answers.

Algebra • Add 3 Addends

 COMMON CORE STANDARD—2.OA.B.2
Add and subtract within 20.

Solve two ways. Circle the two addends you add first.

Circled addends may vary.

1. $2 + 3 + 7 = \underline{12}$ $2 + 3 + 7 = \underline{12}$

2. $5 + 3 + 3 = \underline{11}$ $5 + 3 + 3 = \underline{11}$

3. $4 + 5 + 4 = \underline{13}$ $4 + 5 + 4 = \underline{13}$

4.
$$\begin{array}{r} 5 \\ 4 \\ +\ 5 \\ \hline 14 \end{array} \qquad \begin{array}{r} 5 \\ 4 \\ +\ 5 \\ \hline 14 \end{array}$$

5.
$$\begin{array}{r} 6 \\ 3 \\ +\ 4 \\ \hline 13 \end{array} \qquad \begin{array}{r} 6 \\ 3 \\ +\ 4 \\ \hline 13 \end{array}$$

Problem Solving (Real World)

Choose a way to solve. Write or draw to explain.

6. Amber has 2 red crayons, 5 blue crayons, and 4 yellow crayons. How many crayons does she have?

   $\underline{11}$ crayons

7. **WRITE** ▸ Math Write or draw to explain two ways you can find the sum of $3 + 4 + 5$.

   _____

   Check children's work.

Chapter 3   one hundred eighty-five **185**

Cross-Curricular   S.T.E.M.

Materials small rocks

- Give each small group of children between 10 and 15 small rocks. Discuss some of the characteristics of the rocks, such as color, texture, shape, and size.
- Have children put the rocks into three groups in different ways and write an addition sentence for each way. For example, if they have 13 rocks and put them in one group of 5 and two groups of 4, they would write the addition sentence $5 + 4 + 4 = 13$.

SOCIAL STUDIES

Materials pictures of various national historical locations, such as the White House, Statue of Liberty, and Independence Hall

- Display pictures of places associated with state and national history or government. Discuss why these places are important.
- Give children story problems about visiting these locations. Have children discuss strategies for solving the problems.

  Groups of people tour the White House. In one group there were 3 adults, 5 boys, and 5 girls. How many people were in this group? 13 people

1. What is the sum of
2 + 4 + 6?

<u>12</u>

2. What is the sum of
5 + 4 + 2?

<u>11</u>

3. Write >, <, or = to compare.

688 <u>></u> 648

4. What number can be written
as 4 tens 2 ones?

<u>42</u>

5. What number has the same
value as 50 tens?

<u>500</u>

6. What is the next number in
the pattern?

420, 520, 620, 720, <u>820</u>

© Houghton Mifflin Harcourt Publishing Company

FOR MORE PRACTICE
GO TO THE
Personal Math Trainer

Continue concepts and skills practice with Lesson Check. Use Spiral Review to engage children in previously taught concepts and to promote content retention. Common Core standards are correlated to each section.

Algebra • Relate Addition and Subtraction

FOCUS   COHERENCE   RIGOR

LESSON AT A GLANCE

F C R Focus:

Common Core State Standards

2.OA.B.2 Fluently add and subtract within 20 using mental strategies. By end of Grade 2, know from memory all sums of two one-digit numbers.

MATHEMATICAL PRACTICES (See *Mathematical Practices in GO Math!* in the *Planning Guide* for full text.) **MP2** Reason abstractly and quantitatively. **MP6** Attend to precision. **MP7** Look for and make use of structure. **MP8** Look for and express regularity in repeated reasoning.

F C R Coherence:

Standards Across the Grades

Before	Grade 2	After
1.OA.A.1	2.OA.B.2	3.OA.D.8
1.OA.C.6		

F C R Rigor:

Level 1: Understand Concepts....................*Share and Show* (✓ Checked Items)
Level 2: Procedural Skills and Fluency.......*On Your Own, Practice and Homework*
Level 3: Applications................................*Think Smarter and Go Deeper*

Learning Objective
Use the inverse relationship of addition and subtraction to recall basic facts.

Language Objective
Teams of children brainstorm all the ways that addition and subtraction are related.

Materials
MathBoard

F C R For more about how *GO Math!* fosters **Coherence** within the Content Standards and Mathematical Progressions for this chapter, see page 159J..

About the Math
Professional Development

Progress to Algebra
Using Bar Models

A bar model is a visual tool used to organize information in a problem.

The top diagram shows that two parts comprise the whole: part + part = whole.

The middle diagram shows a bar model for this addition problem.

Hudson sees 3 bugs on a leaf and 7 bugs on the sidewalk. How many bugs does Hudson see in all?

• The two parts are known, so they are added to find the whole: 10 bugs in all.

The bottom diagram shows a bar model for this subtraction problem.

Charlotte collected 13 shells at the beach. She gave 5 shells to her brother. How many shells does Charlotte have now?

• The whole and one part are known, subtract to find the missing part: 8 shells.

 Professional Development Videos

part	part

whole

3	7

10

5	8

13

Daily Routines

Common Core

 **Problem of the Day 3.5**

Number of the Day 247

Draw a quick picture to show the value of each digit in the number. Children's drawings should show 2 hundreds, 4 tens, and 7 ones.

Have children share their pictures and identify the place value of each digit.

Vocabulary **differences**

 • Interactive Student Edition
• Multimedia eGlossary

Fluency Task

Materials: connecting cubes

Have children represent each of the following facts using connecting cubes. They should build the biggest number first and then break away the second number to find the third.

- **10 − 3 = 7**
- **9 − 4 = 5**
- **14 − 7 = 7**
- **15 − 6 = 9**

① ENGAGE

with the Interactive Student Edition

Essential Question
How are addition and subtraction related?

Making Connections
Ask children what they know about subtraction facts.

Have you used subtraction facts before? Answers may vary.
When might you need to subtract one number from another? Sample answers: when you are giving objects away or taking a group of objects apart.

Learning Activity
What is the problem the children are trying to solve? Connect the story to the problem. Ask the following questions.

- **What does the word "difference" mean?** Sample answer: the answer in a subtraction problem.

- **How are addition facts related to subtraction facts?** Sample answer: you can subtract one addend from the sum and the answer is the other addend.

Literacy and Mathematics
View the lesson opener with the children. Then, choose one or more of the following activities:

- Have children write a story about subtraction or taking away using numbers less than 20. Have them underline each number involved in the subtraction.

- Have children represent the number 13 using connecting cubes. Have them experiment with different ways of breaking the number apart and write subtraction facts to match each way they find.

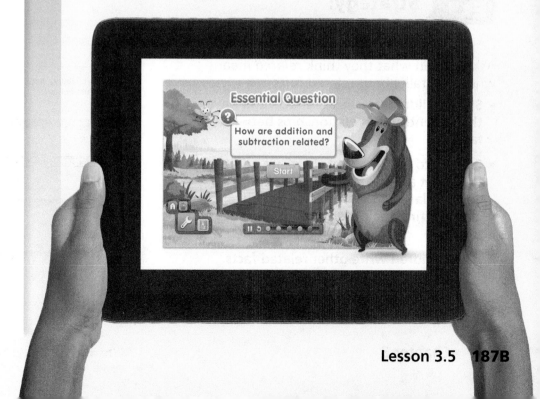

② EXPLORE

Listen and Draw  Common Core MATHEMATICAL PRACTICES

MP7 Look for and make use of structure. Read the first exercise. Have children complete the first bar model.

The soccer team has 8 red balls and 7 yellow balls. How many soccer balls does the team have? 15 soccer balls

Direct children's attention to the bracket below the bars. Explain that the bracket shows that the two bars for the parts are being joined to show the whole.

- **How does the bar model at the top of the page help you solve the problem?** Possible answer: The model shows that I need to find the whole.

- **Will you add or subtract to solve for the missing amount?** add

Read the related subtraction problem.

The soccer team has 15 balls inside the locker room. The children took the 7 yellow balls outside. How many soccer balls were inside? 8 soccer balls

- **What information is missing in the bar model for this problem?** the number of soccer balls inside

- **Will you add or subtract to solve for the missing amount?** subtract

 MP6 Attend to precision. Use Math Talk to focus on children's understanding of the differences between addition and subtraction.

Name _____

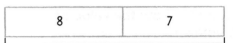

Lesson 3.5

Algebra • Relate Addition and Subtraction

Common Core **Operations and Algebraic Thinking—2.OA.B.2**
MATHEMATICAL PRACTICES
MP2, MP6, MP8

Essential Question How are addition and subtraction related?

 Listen and Draw

Complete the bar model to show the problem. Check children's work.

8	7

_____15_____

| 15 | soccer balls |

Problem Type:
Put Together/Take Apart •
Total Unknown

_____15_____ soccer balls

8	7

15

Problem Type:
Take From • Result Unknown

_____8_____ soccer balls

 Math Talk: Possible answer: The bar models are the same, except that the whole was missing in the first problem and a part was missing in the second problem.

FOR THE TEACHER • Read the following problems. Have children complete the bar model for each. The soccer team has 8 red balls and 7 yellow balls. How many soccer balls does the team have? The soccer team has 15 balls inside the locker room. The children took the 7 yellow balls outside. How many soccer balls were inside?

Math Talk MATHEMATICAL PRACTICES 6

Explain how the bar models for the problems are alike and how they are different.

Chapter 3

one hundred eighty-seven **187**

© Houghton Mifflin Harcourt Publishing Company

ELL **Strategy:**
Identify Relationships

Ask children what they think *related* means when you talk about related facts.

- **Show children two related facts and have them identify the relationships between the facts.**

- **Explain to children that there are addition facts that are related to subtraction facts. These related addition facts can help children find the difference for a subtraction fact.**

- **Have children write other related facts.**

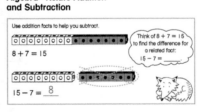 Reteach 3.5 ▲ RtI

Name _____
Lesson 3.5 Reteach

Algebra • Relate Addition and Subtraction

Use addition facts to help you subtract.

$8 + 7 = 15$

Think of $8 + 7 = 15$ to find the difference for a related fact.
$15 - 7 = $

$15 - 7 = \underline{8}$

Write the sum and the difference for the related facts.

1. $6 + 3 = \underline{9}$
   $9 - 6 = \underline{3}$

2. $7 + 6 = \underline{13}$
   $13 - 7 = \underline{6}$

3. $6 + 8 = \underline{14}$
   $14 - 8 = \underline{6}$

4. $7 + 4 = \underline{11}$
   $11 - 7 = \underline{4}$

5. $8 + 4 = \underline{12}$
   $12 - 4 = \underline{8}$

6. $8 + 8 = \underline{16}$
   $16 - 8 = \underline{8}$

7. $9 + 7 = \underline{16}$
   $16 - 7 = \underline{9}$

8. $7 + 5 = \underline{12}$
   $12 - 7 = \underline{5}$

Chapter Resources 3-13 Reteach
© Houghton Mifflin Harcourt Publishing Company

Enrich 3.5 **Differentiated Instruction**

Name _____
Lesson 3.5 Enrich

Related Facts

A sum and one addend are written in the triangle. Write the other addend. Then write an addition fact and a related subtraction fact for the numbers.

Facts may vary. Possible answers are given.

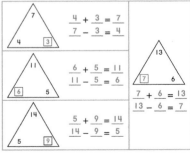

Triangle: 7, 4, 3
$\underline{4} + \underline{3} = 7$
$7 - \underline{3} = \underline{4}$

Triangle: 11, 6, 5
$\underline{6} + \underline{5} = 11$
$11 - \underline{5} = \underline{6}$

Triangle: 13, 7, 6
$\underline{7} + \underline{6} = 13$
$13 - \underline{6} = \underline{7}$

Triangle: 14, 5, 9
$\underline{5} + \underline{9} = 14$
$14 - \underline{9} = \underline{5}$

 Writing and Reasoning Draw another triangle with a sum and one addend. Have a partner write the missing addend and the related addition and subtraction facts.

Check children's work.

Chapter Resources 3-14 Enrich
© Houghton Mifflin Harcourt Publishing Company

Model and Draw

You can use addition facts to remember **differences**. Related facts have the same whole and parts.

> Think of the addends in an addition fact to find the difference for a related subtraction fact.

6	7

13

$6 + 7 = \underline{13}$

6	7

13

$13 - 7 = \underline{6}$

Share and Show

Write the sum and the difference for the related facts.

1. $5 + 4 = \underline{9}$
   $9 - 4 = \underline{5}$

2. $2 + 7 = \underline{9}$
   $9 - 2 = \underline{7}$

3. $3 + 8 = \underline{11}$
   $11 - 8 = \underline{3}$

4. $5 + 8 = \underline{13}$
   $13 - 5 = \underline{8}$

5. $\underline{9} = 1 + 8$
   $\underline{8} = 9 - 1$

6. $9 + 9 = \underline{18}$
   $18 - 9 = \underline{9}$

7. $\underline{15} = 8 + 7$
   $\underline{7} = 15 - 8$

8. $4 + 7 = \underline{11}$
   $11 - 7 = \underline{4}$

9. $7 + 5 = \underline{12}$
   $12 - 7 = \underline{5}$

© Houghton Mifflin Harcourt Publishing Company

188 one hundred eighty-eight

Model and Draw  MATHEMATICAL PRACTICES

MP8 Look for and express regularity in repeated reasoning. Use the bar models to discuss the whole and the parts in the related facts.

- **How are the addition fact and the subtraction fact alike?** They have the same whole, 13, and the same parts, 6 and 7.

- **How can knowing 6 + 7 = 13 help you find the difference for 13 − 7?** Possible answer: I can think about how the facts are related. They have the same whole and one part is the same, so the other part must also be the same. 13 − 7 = 6

- **Why are the answers for the two problems written in different places on the bar models?** Possible answer: The first problem is an addition problem and we are finding the whole; the second problem is a subtraction problem and we are finding a part.

③ EXPLAIN

Share and Show

Connect Exercises 1–9 to the learning model.

- **In Exercise 1, how are the two number sentences related?** Possible answer: They have the same whole and the same parts.

Use the checked exercises for **Quick Check**. Children should use their MathBoards to show their solutions to these exercises.

 Quick Check RtI

If a child misses the checked exercises

Then Differentiate Instruction with
- Reteach 3.5
- Personal Math trainer 2.OA.B.2
- RtI Tier 1 Activity (online)

⚠ COMMON ERRORS

Error Children do not understand the inverse relationship between addition and subtraction.

Example 3 + 6 = 9   9 − 6 = 9

Springboard to Learning Have children use connecting cubes to model the addition fact and then break apart the train to model and solve the subtraction fact.

Advanced Learners   🕐 Visual / Individual / Partners

Materials index cards

- Have children use the numbers 1 to 18 to write a subtraction sentence on an index card, with the difference left blank. Ask: **What related addition fact could help you solve the subtraction problem?**

- Have children write a related addition sentence on the card using the two numbers given and a missing addend.

- Have children trade cards and fill in the missing numbers. Remind children that the two missing numbers on each card should be the same.

  $14 - 6 = \underline{}$
  $6 + \underline{} = 14$

④ ELABORATE

On Your Own

If a child answers the checked exercises correctly, assign Exercises 10–25.

MP6 Attend to precision. In Exercises 22–25 children use higher order thinking skills to write a related subtraction fact for an addition fact.

- **How do you use the addition fact to help you write a related subtraction fact?** Possible answer: The addition fact shows the two parts added together to make the whole. For a subtraction fact, I write the whole with one part subtracted from it and the other part as the difference.

You may wish to ask children to write both subtraction facts and the second addition fact related to each addition fact.

Most children are not accustomed to seeing related facts with the sum or difference listed on the left side of the equal sign. Ask children to write the related facts in Exercises 22–25 both ways.

Go DEEPER

Challenge children to make mathematical connections by writing a story problem for the related facts in one of the Exercises 22–25. Have children draw bar models to show the related facts.

Name _____

On Your Own

Write the sum and the difference for the related facts.

10. $4 + 3 = \underline{7}$
$7 - 3 = \underline{4}$

11. $2 + 6 = \underline{8}$
$8 - 6 = \underline{2}$

12. $6 + 4 = \underline{10}$
$10 - 6 = \underline{4}$

13. $7 + 3 = \underline{10}$
$10 - 7 = \underline{3}$

14. $8 + 6 = \underline{14}$
$14 - 6 = \underline{8}$

15. $\underline{12} = 3 + 9$
$\underline{3} = 12 - 9$

16. $6 + 5 = \underline{11}$
$11 - 5 = \underline{6}$

17. $7 + 7 = \underline{14}$
$14 - 7 = \underline{7}$

18. $9 + 6 = \underline{15}$
$15 - 9 = \underline{6}$

19. $5 + 9 = \underline{14}$
$14 - 9 = \underline{5}$

20. $\underline{12} = 4 + 8$
$\underline{8} = 12 - 4$

21. $9 + 7 = \underline{16}$
$16 - 7 = \underline{9}$

MATHEMATICAL PRACTICE ⑥   Make Connections

Write a related subtraction fact for each addition fact.

22. $7 + 8 = 15$
$15 - 8 = 7$ or
$15 - 7 = 8$
_____

23. $5 + 7 = 12$
$12 - 7 = 5$ or
$12 - 5 = 7$
_____

24. $6 + 7 = 13$
$13 - 7 = 6$ or
$13 - 6 = 7$
_____

25. $9 + 8 = 17$
$17 - 8 = 9$ or
$17 - 9 = 8$
_____

Chapter 3 • Lesson 5   one hundred eighty-nine **189**

© Houghton Mifflin Harcourt Publishing Company • Image Credits: ©Teguh Mujiono/Shutterstock

---

PROBLEM TYPE SITUATIONS

Addition and Subtraction

Take From • Result Unknown
Exercise: 27

Put Together/Take Apart • Total Unknown
Exercise: 27

Put Together/Take Apart • Addend Unknown
Exercise: 28

Compare • Difference Unknown
Exercise: 26

Problem Solving • Applications   WRITE) Math

Solve. Write or draw to explain.

26. Trevor has 7 kites. Pam has 4 kites. How many more kites does Trevor have than Pam?

_____3_____ more kites

27. **THINK SMARTER** Mr. Sims has a bag of 7 pears and a bag of 6 pears. His family eats 5 pears. How many pears does he have now?

_____8_____ pears

28. **THINK SMARTER** Elin counts 7 geese in the water and some geese on the shore. There are 16 geese in all. Draw a picture to show the two groups of geese.

> Check children's work. Drawings should show a group of 7 and a group of 9.

Write a number sentence that can help you find how many geese are on the shore.   Some possible answers are given.

$$7 + 9 = 16 \text{ or } 16 - 7 = 9$$

How many geese are on the shore?   _____9_____ geese

TAKE HOME ACTIVITY • Ask your child to name some subtraction facts that he or she knows well.

190 one hundred ninety

© Houghton Mifflin Harcourt Publishing Company • Image Credits: (c) ©Getty Images/Photodisc

---

Problem Solving • Applications Real World

Common Core MATHEMATICAL PRACTICES

Have children read Exercise 26. Ask them to describe how they will solve the problem.

THINK SMARTER

A key to solving Exercise 27 is recognizing that it is a multistep problem that can be solved by using both addition and subtraction.

Math on the Spot Video Tutor

Use this video to help children model and solve this type of *Think Smarter* problem.

GO DIGITAL **Math on the Spot** videos are in the Interactive Student Edition and at *www.thinkcentral.com*.

THINK SMARTER

Children may understand that their drawing should show one group of 7 but not understand how to represent the other group. They will be able to draw a picture that correctly represents the problem situation for Exercise 28 if they understand that 16 is the whole for a number sentence. Guide children to understand that the value of the other group is an unknown addend in an addition fact or the difference in a subtraction fact.

5 EVALUATE Formative Assessment

Essential Question

Reflect Using the Language Objective Have teams of children brainstorm to answer the Essential Question.

How are addition and subtraction related?
Possible answer: Addition and subtraction undo each other; related addition and subtraction facts have the same whole and parts.

Math Journal   WRITE) Math

Write a related subtraction fact for 3 + 9 = 12. Explain how the two facts are related.

 DIFFERENTIATED INSTRUCTION   **INDEPENDENT ACTIVITIES**

Grab-and-Go!
Differentiated Centers Kit

Activities
Canine Collection

Children complete purple Activity Card 3 by writing related facts using various sets of numbers.

Literature
Game Time!

Children read the book and add or subtract to find shin guards for the soccer players.

Games
Caterpillar Chase

Games

Children practice basic addition facts to move along the game path.

Practice and Homework

Use the Practice and Homework pages to provide children with more practice of the concepts and skills presented in this lesson. Children master their understanding as they complete practice items and then challenge their critical thinking skills with Problem Solving. Use the Write Math section to determine children's understanding of content for this lesson. Encourage children to use their Math Journals to record their answers.

Algebra • Relate Addition and Subtraction

COMMON CORE STANDARD—2.OA.B.2
Add and subtract within 20.

Write the sum and the difference for the related facts.

1. $9 + 6 = \underline{15}$

   $15 - 6 = \underline{9}$

2. $8 + 5 = \underline{13}$

   $13 - 5 = \underline{8}$

3. $9 + 9 = \underline{18}$

   $18 - 9 = \underline{9}$

4. $7 + 3 = \underline{10}$

   $10 - 3 = \underline{7}$

5. $7 + 5 = \underline{12}$

   $12 - 5 = \underline{7}$

6. $6 + 8 = \underline{14}$

   $14 - 6 = \underline{8}$

7. $6 + 7 = \underline{13}$

   $13 - 6 = \underline{7}$

8. $8 + 8 = \underline{16}$

   $16 - 8 = \underline{8}$

9. $6 + 4 = \underline{10}$

   $10 - 4 = \underline{6}$

Problem Solving

Solve. Write or draw to explain.

10. There are 13 children on the bus. Then 5 children get off the bus. How many children are on the bus now?

    $\underline{8}$ children

11. **WRITE Math** Write a related subtraction fact for $9 + 3 = 12$. Explain how the two facts are related.

    Check children's work. _____

© Houghton Mifflin Harcourt Publishing Company

Common Core **PROFESSIONAL DEVELOPMENT**

Mathematical Practices in Your Classroom

CC.K–12.MP3 Construct viable arguments and critique the reasoning of others.

Throughout this chapter, children are reviewing and applying various strategies to find sums and differences for basic facts. In this lesson, the relationship between addition and subtraction is reviewed.

Children must understand this inverse relationship from the vantage point of related facts having the same whole and parts. It is much more than just knowing that the same three numbers are used in related facts; it is a deeper understanding of what addition and subtraction are, and *why* certain sets of facts are related.

This deeper understanding can help increase children's fluency with basic facts and with multidigit computation in later chapters.

Encourage children's participation in a discussion.

- **Describe what happens in an addition fact when you have two parts and a whole.** Possible answer: In an addition fact, the two parts are added together and their sum is the whole. **Describe what happens in a subtraction fact with the two parts and the whole.** Possible answer: In a subtraction fact, you start with the whole, take away one part, and the other part is left.

- **What does it mean when someone says that addition and subtraction undo each other?** Possible answer: When you add two parts together to find the whole, and then subtract one of those parts from the whole, you end up with the other part.

- Write $4 + 5 = 9$ and $9 - 2 = 7$ on the board. Ask: **Are these facts related? Explain.** Check children's explanations. Encourage children to analyze each other's reasoning.

Some children may have difficulty verbalizing the inverse relationship of addition and subtraction. Suggest that they use drawings or counters to help show their reasoning.

Lesson Check (2.OA.B.2)

1. Write a related addition fact for
15 − 6 = 9.

Possible answer:

__9__ + __6__ = __15__

2. Write a related subtraction fact
for 5 + 7 = 12.

Possible answer:

__12__ − __7__ = __5__

Spiral Review (2.NBT.A.1, 2.NBT.A.3, 2.NBT.B.8)

3. What is another way to
write 4 hundreds?

__400__

4. What is the next number in
the pattern?

515, 615, 715, 815, __915__

5. What number is 10 more
than 237?

__247__

6. Write the number 110 as a sum
of hundreds and tens.

__100__ + __10__

FOR MORE PRACTICE
GO TO THE
Personal Math Trainer

© Houghton Mifflin Harcourt Publishing Company

Continue concepts and skills practice with
Lesson Check. Use Spiral Review to engage
children in previously taught concepts and to
promote content retention. Common Core
standards are correlated to each section.

Practice Subtraction Facts

LESSON AT A GLANCE

FOCUS COHERENCE RIGOR

F C R Focus:

Common Core State Standards

2.OA.B.2 Fluently add and subtract within 20 using mental strategies. By end of Grade 2, know from memory all sums of two one-digit numbers.

MATHEMATICAL PRACTICES (See *Mathematical Practices in GO Math!* in the *Planning Guide* for full text.)
MP1 Make sense of problems and persevere in solving them. **MP3** Construct viable arguments and critique the reasoning of others. **MP4** Model with mathematics.

F C R Coherence:

Standards Across the Grades

Before	Grade 2	After
1.OA.A.1	2.OA.B.2	3.OA.D.8
1.OA.C.6		

F C R Rigor:

Level 1: Understand Concepts....................*Share and Show* (Checked Items)
Level 2: Procedural Skills and Fluency.......*On Your Own, Practice and Homework*
Level 3: Applications..................................*Think Smarter and Go Deeper*

Learning Objective
Recall differences for basic facts using mental strategies.

Language Objective
Children recommend in their Math Journal two of the best ways to remember differences.

Materials
MathBoard

F C R For more about how *GO Math!* fosters **Coherence** within the Content Standards and Mathematical Progressions for this chapter, see page 159J.

About the Math
Professional Development

Progress to Algebra
If Children Ask

Children may question why thinking about addition facts can be a good strategy to use to solve subtraction facts.

Review with children how related addition and subtraction facts have the same whole and the same parts.

For the basic fact 6 + 9 = 15, the parts are the addends, 6 and 9; the whole is the sum, 15. Thinking about the addends (or the parts) in this addition fact can help children find the difference (one of the parts) for the related subtraction fact, 15 − 9 = _____.

This addition/subtraction connection is a powerful mathematical tool and can be a very useful strategy for recalling basic facts.

 Professional Development Videos

GO DIGITAL

 Interactive Student Edition

 Personal Math Trainer

 Math on the Spot Video

 Animated Math Models

iT *i*Tools: Counters

MM HMH Mega Math

① ENGAGE

with the Interactive Student Edition

Essential Question
What are some ways to remember differences?

Making Connections
Ask children to discuss what they have learned about subtraction facts.

What are some of the subtraction facts that you learned in Lesson 5? Check children's responses. **How do addition facts relate to subtraction facts?** Sample answer: You can use an addition fact to write a subtraction fact by subtracting one addend from the sum and writing the answer as the other addend.

Learning Activity
What is the problem the children are trying to solve? Connect the story to the problem. Ask the following questions.

- **How many addition facts relate to the subtraction fact 15 − 9 = 6? Write them.** Two; 9 + 6 = 15 and 6 + 9 = 15

- **Can you write another subtraction fact using the same numbers? If so, write it.** Yes; 15 − 6 = 9

Literacy and Mathematics
View the lesson opener with the children. Then, choose one or more of the following activities:

- Have children write a story involving two subtraction facts. Have them circle the numbers in the facts using a red crayon.

- Have children use connecting cubes to represent a subtraction fact of their choosing. Then have them write all related addition and subtraction facts.

EXPLORE

Progress to Algebra → **2.OA.B.2** Fluently add and subtract within 20 using mental strategies. By end of Grade 2, know from memory all sums of two one-digit numbers.

Listen and Draw Real World · Hands On

Common Core **MATHEMATICAL PRACTICES**

MP4 Model with mathematics.
Tell children that Gina put 4 color tiles inside the circle and then put 3 color tiles outside the circle.

- **What addition fact could be written for Gina's model?** Possible answers: 4 + 3 = 7, or 3 + 4 = 7

- **How does this addition fact show Gina's model?** Possible answer: It shows the two parts added together to make the whole. The number of tiles inside the circle and the number of tiles outside the circle are the parts. The total number of tiles is the whole.

Have children look at the picture of Gina's model. Tell them that Gina put 3 color tiles outside the circle and 4 color tiles inside the circle.

- **What addition fact could be written for Gina's model?** Possible answers: 4 + 3 = 7, or 3 + 4 = 7

Now have children look again at the picture of Gina's model. Tell them that there were 7 tiles outside the circle. Then Gina moved 4 of the tiles to be inside the circle.

- **What subtraction fact could be written for Gina's model?** 7 − 4 = 3

Now have children look again at the picture of Gina's model. Tell them that there were 7 tiles inside the circle. Then Gina moved 3 of the tiles to be outside the circle.

- **What subtraction fact could be written for Gina's model?** 7 − 3 = 4

Math Talk **MP3 Construct viable arguments and critique the reasoning of others.** Use Math Talk to focus on children's understanding of how addition and subtraction facts are related.

ELL **Strategy:**
Develop Meanings

Show children a subtraction problem with a missing difference.

- **Then show them a set of facts in which only one fact helps find the difference of the subtraction.** Have children point to the fact that helps them find the difference.

- **Use the word** *difference* **to describe the answer to a subtraction problem.**

- **Have children use the word difference to describe another subtraction problem.**

193 Chapter 3

Name _____

Lesson 3.6

Practice Subtraction Facts

Essential Question What are some ways to remember differences?

Common Core **Operations and Algebraic Thinking—2.OA.B.2**
MATHEMATICAL PRACTICES
MP1, MP3

 **Listen and Draw** Real World

Use Gina's model to answer the question.

Problem Type:
Put Together/Take Apart • Total Unknown

Gina's Model

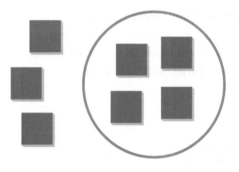

4 + 3 = 7 or 3 + 4 = 7	4 + 3 = 7 or 3 + 4 = 7
7 − 4 = 3	7 − 3 = 4

Math Talk: All four facts use the same whole and the same parts.

 FOR THE TEACHER • Tell children that Gina put 4 color tiles inside the circle and then put 3 color tiles outside the circle. Then ask: What addition fact could be written for Gina's model? Repeat with stories for the three facts that are related to this addition fact.

Math Talk MATHEMATICAL PRACTICES ③

Compare Strategies Explain how the different facts for Gina's model are related.

Chapter 3   one hundred ninety-three **193**

© Houghton Mifflin Harcourt Publishing Company

Reteach 3.6 ▲ **RtI**

Name _____

Lesson 3.6 Reteach

Practice Subtraction Facts

Here are two ways to find differences.

10 − 3 = ___?___

Count back 1, 2, or 3.

5 6 7 8 9 10 11

Think of a related addition fact.

10 − 1 = 9
10 − 2 = 8
10 − 3 = 7

3 + 7 = 10
so, 10 − 3 = 7

Write the difference.

1. 13 − 5 = 8   2. 10 − 4 = 6

3. 12 − 3 = 9   4. 11 − 2 = 9

5. 9 − 3 = 6   6. 12 − 5 = 7

7. 16 − 8 = 8   8. 13 − 7 = 6

Chapter Resources 3-15 Reteach
© Houghton Mifflin Harcourt Publishing Company

Enrich 3.6 ◀ **Differentiated Instruction**

Name _____

Lesson 3.6 Enrich

Subtracting Across and Down

Each box has four subtraction sentences. Two are written across. The other two are written down.

Fill in the missing numbers so that each subtraction sentence is correct.

1.
12	−	6	=	6
−				
8				5
=				=
4	−	3	=	1

2.
8	−	3	=	5
−				
4				5
=				=
4	−	4	=	0

3.
13	−	5	=	8
−				
4				3
=				=
9	−	4	=	5

4.
10	−	3	=	7
−				
6				4
=				=
4	−	1	=	3

 Writing and Reasoning How did you find the missing numbers in the top row in Exercise 4?

Possible answer: First I found the missing number in the bottom row and then I worked backward.

Chapter Resources 3-16 Enrich
© Houghton Mifflin Harcourt Publishing Company

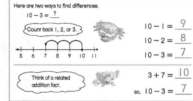

Model and Draw

These are some ways to find differences.

You can count back by 1, 2, or 3.

$7 - 2 = \underline{5}$ Start with 7. Say: 6, 5.

$9 - 3 = \underline{6}$ Start with 9. Say: 8, 7, 6.

You can think about a missing addend to subtract.

$8 - 5 = \blacksquare$ $5 + 3 = 8$

So, $8 - 5 = \underline{3}$.

Share and Show

Write the difference.

1. $6 - 4 = \underline{2}$
2. $10 - 7 = \underline{3}$
3. $\underline{3} = 5 - 2$
4. $14 - 6 = \underline{8}$
5. $\underline{4} = 8 - 4$
6. $11 - 3 = \underline{8}$
7. $\underline{2} = 7 - 5$
8. $10 - 4 = \underline{6}$
9. $5 - 0 = \underline{5}$
10. $13 - 9 = \underline{4}$
11. $9 - 3 = \underline{6}$
12. $\underline{1} = 7 - 6$
13. $12 - 3 = \underline{9}$
14. $6 - 3 = \underline{3}$
15. $9 - 5 = \underline{4}$
16. $10 - 6 = \underline{4}$
17. $\underline{5} = 8 - 3$
18. $13 - 5 = \underline{8}$

Model and Draw MATHEMATICAL PRACTICES

MP1 Make sense of problems and persevere in solving them. Work through the two strategies and examples with children.

- **Why would someone use the count back strategy when subtracting 1, 2, or 3?** Possible answer: It is quick and easy to count back by 1, 2, or 3.

- **How does knowing 5 + 3 = 8 help you to find the difference for 8 − 5?** Possible answer: They are related facts and have the same whole, 8, and the same parts, 5 and 3. So, 8 − 5 = 3.

- **What other strategy could you use to find the difference for 8 − 5?** Possible answer: I could count up from 5 to 8 to get 3.

③ EXPLAIN

Share and Show

Connect Exercises 1–18 to the learning model.

- **What strategy can you use to solve Exercise 1?** Possible answer: I can think of the related addition fact. 4 + 2 = 6, so 6 − 4 = 2.

Use the checked exercises for **Quick Check**. Children should use their MathBoards to show their solutions to these exercises.

✓ Quick Check   RtI

If a child misses the checked exercises

Then Differentiate Instruction with
- Reteach 3.6
- Personal Math trainer 2.OA.B.2
- RtI Tier 1 Activity (online)

⚠ COMMON ERRORS

Error Children use the count back strategy with numbers greater than 3 and lose count.

Example $7 - 4 = 4$

Springboard to Learning Have children describe how they got their answer. Show them how to use one of the related facts strategies to solve the problem. For example, $3 + 4 = 7$, so $7 - 4 = 3$.

Lesson 3.6 194

On Your Own

If a child answers the checked exercises correctly, assign Exercises 19–34.

 THINK SMARTER

Be sure to assign this exercise to students in the Personal Math Trainer. It features an animation to help them model and answer the exercise. In Exercise 34 children solve three sets of four facts, look for the patterns in the facts, and then write the next fact in the pattern.

- **Describe the patterns in the fact in the first column of Exercise 34.** Possible answer: The first number in each fact is 2 less than the first number in the fact before it. 1 is being subtracted in each fact. Each difference is 2 less than the difference in the fact before it.

 **Math on the Spot
Video Tutor**
Use this video to help children model and solve this type of *Think Smarter* problem.

GO DIGITAL **Math on the Spot** videos are in the Interactive Student Edition and at *www.thinkcentral.com*.

GO DEEPER

MP3 Construct viable arguments and critique the reasoning of others. Give children the subtraction expressions below. Ask them to identify a strategy that they can use to find each difference.

11 − 9	8 − 3	5 − 4	10 − 7
6 − 5	8 − 2	10 − 5	9 − 6

5 EVALUATE Formative Assessment

Essential Question

Reflect Using the Language Objective Have children recommend in their Math Journal two answers to the Essential Question.

What are some ways to remember differences? Possible answer: I could use a related addition fact or count back by 1, 2, or 3.

Math Journal WRITE ▸ Math

Write or draw to explain two different ways to find the difference for 12 − 3.

Name _____

On Your Own

Write the difference.

19. 11 − 2 = __9__   20. 9 − 7 = __2__   21. __3__ = 7 − 4

22. 12 − 5 = __7__   23. 8 − 6 = __2__   24. __7__ = 7 − 0

25. __5__ = 10 − 5   26. 15 − 8 = __7__   27. 13 − 7 = __6__

28. 10 − 8 = __2__   29. 8 − 5 = __3__   30. __3__ = 9 − 6

31. __5__ = 9 − 4   32. 11 − 8 = __3__   33. 12 − 7 = __5__

34. **THINK** SMARTER
Write the differences. Then write the next fact in the pattern.

10 − 1 = 9	12 − 9 = 3	18 − 9 = 9
8 − 1 = 7	13 − 9 = 4	17 − 8 = 9
6 − 1 = 5	14 − 9 = 5	16 − 7 = 9
4 − 1 = 3	15 − 9 = 6	15 − 6 = 9
2 − 1 = 1	16 − 9 = 7	14 − 5 = 9

 TAKE HOME ACTIVITY • With your child, practice saying subtraction facts from this lesson.

Chapter 3 • Lesson 6   one hundred ninety-five **195**

DIFFERENTIATED INSTRUCTION   **INDEPENDENT ACTIVITIES**

Differentiated Centers Kit

Activities
A Heap of Sheep

Children complete orange Activity Card 3 by solving a two-part subtraction problem using numbers through 18.

Activities
Benny, Bessie, and the Blueberries

Children read the book and find how two bears share 16 blueberries.

Literature
On the Ferris Wheel

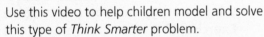
Games

Children practice basic subtraction facts to move along the game path.

Name _____

✓ **Mid-Chapter Checkpoint**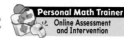
Personal Math Trainer
Online Assessment and Intervention

Concepts and Skills

Write the sum. (2.OA.B.2)

1. $3 + 6 =$ __9__   2. $8 + 0 =$ __8__   3. $7 + 7 =$ __14__

4. $9 + 4 =$ __13__   5. __11__ $= 5 + 6$ 6. $2 + 8 =$ __10__

7. $3 + 7 + 2 =$ __12__   8. $4 + 4 + 6 =$ __14__

Show how you can make a ten to find the sum.
Write the sum. (2.OA.B.2)

9. $9 + 7 =$ __16__   10. $6 + 8 =$ __14__

$10 + $ __6__ $= $ __16__ $10 + $ __4__ $= $ __14__

Write the sum and the difference for the related facts. (2.OA.B.2)

11. $5 + 4 =$ __9__   12. $3 + 9 =$ __12__   13. $8 + 7 =$ __15__

$9 - 4 =$ __5__ $12 - 9 =$ __3__ $15 - 8 =$ __7__

14. **THINK SMARTER** Lily has 6 toys cars.
Yong has 5 toy cars. How many
toy cars do they have? (2.OA.B.2)

__11__ toy cars

© Houghton Mifflin Harcourt Publishing Company

Formative Assessment

Use the **Mid-Chapter Checkpoint** to assess children's learning and progress in the first half of the chapter. The formative assessment provides the opportunity to adjust teaching methods for individual or whole class instruction.

THINK SMARTER

This exercises children's ability to find a sum in a real-world context. Have children explain to you how they will find the addition fact necessary to solve the problem.

✓ **Data-Driven Decision Making** ▲ **RtI**

Based on the results of the Mid-Chapter Checkpoint, use the following resources to strengthen individual or whole class instruction.

Item	Lesson	Standard	Common Error	Personal Math Trainer	Intervene with
1–6	3.1, 3.2	2.OA.B.2	May add incorrectly	2.OA.B.2	R—3.1, R—3.2
7, 8	3.4	2.OA.B.2	May find the sum of two addends and forget to add the third	2.OA.B.2	R—3.4
9, 10	3.3	2.OA.B.2	May break apart the addend incorrectly	2.OA.B.2	R—3.3
11–13	3.5	2.OA.B.2	May not understand the inverse relationship of addition and subtraction	2.OA.B.2	R—3.5
14	3.6	2.OA.B.2	May add incorrectly	2.OA.B.2	R—3.6

Key: R—Reteach (in the *Chapter Resources*)

Practice and Homework

Use the Practice and Homework pages to provide children with more practice of the concepts and skills presented in this lesson. Children master their understanding as they complete practice items and then challenge their critical thinking skills with Problem Solving. Use the Write Math section to determine children's understanding of content for this lesson. Encourage children to use their Math Journals to record their answers.

Practice Subtraction Facts

Common Core   COMMON CORE STANDARD—2.OA.B.2
Add and subtract within 20.

Write the difference.

1. $15 - 9 = \underline{6}$

2. $10 - 2 = \underline{8}$

3. $\underline{8} = 13 - 5$

4. $14 - 7 = \underline{7}$

5. $10 - 8 = \underline{2}$

6. $12 - 7 = \underline{5}$

7. $\underline{7} = 10 - 3$

8. $16 - 7 = \underline{9}$

9. $8 - 4 = \underline{4}$

10. $11 - 5 = \underline{6}$

11. $13 - 6 = \underline{7}$

12. $\underline{3} = 12 - 9$

13. $16 - 9 = \underline{7}$

14. $\underline{2} = 11 - 9$

15. $12 - 8 = \underline{4}$

Problem Solving (Real World)

Solve. Write or draw to explain.

16. Mr. Li has 16 pencils. He gives 9 pencils to some students. How many pencils does Mr. Li have now?

$\underline{7}$ pencils

17. **WRITE** ▸ Math Write or draw to explain two different ways to find the difference for $12 - 3$.

_____

Check children's work.

© Houghton Mifflin Harcourt Publishing Company

Lesson Check (2.OA.B.2)

1. Write the difference.

$$13 - 6 = \underline{7}$$

2. Write the difference.

$$12 - 3 = \underline{9}$$

Spiral Review (2.NBT.A.1, 2.NBT.A.1a, 2.NBT.A.1b, 2.NBT.A.2, 2.NBT.A.3)

3. What is the value of the underlined digit?

6<u>2</u>5

<u>20</u>

4. Count by fives.

405, <u>410</u>, <u>415</u>, <u>420</u>

5. Devin has 39 toy blocks. What is the value of the digit 9 in this number?

<u>9</u>

6. Which number has the same value as 20 tens?

<u>200</u>

198 one hundred ninety-eight

FOR MORE PRACTICE
GO TO THE
Personal Math Trainer

Continue concepts and skills practice with Lesson Check. Use Spiral Review to engage children in previously taught concepts and to promote content retention. Common Core standards are correlated to each section.

Monitoring Common Core Success

Maintaining Focus on the Major Work

Part of the major work in Grade 2 is addition and subtraction within 20 (2.OA.B). Building upon the conceptual understanding of addition, children continue to expand their development in Lessons 3.1–3.4 by learning strategies such as using doubles facts to find sums for near doubles, changing the order or grouping of addends, and breaking apart an addend to make the other addend a ten. They extend their knowledge of subtraction by using addition facts to find differences in Lessons 3.5 and 3.6. Exercises in Lessons 3.1–3.6 involve addition and subtraction within 20 using mental strategies (2.OA.B.2). Practicing these strategies and skills is a vital component toward the mastery of major work 2.OA.B.

Connecting Content Across Domains and Clusters

In Lessons 3.1–3.6, children mainly focus on a single cluster, 2.OA.B. While working in this cluster, children strengthen their understanding of addition and subtraction within 20. In Lesson 3.3, children use the make a ten strategy to find sums, and in Lesson 3.4, they apply the Commutative and Associative Properties of Addition to find sums of three addends. This work directly connects to another major cluster, 2.OA.A, in which children are required to represent and solve problems involving addition and subtraction.

Building Fluency

Children are building fluency in 2.OA.B.2 (add and subtract within 20) and 2.NBT.B.5 (add and subtract within 100) while working in Lessons 3.1–3.6. Mathematical Practices abstract reasoning (MP2) and modeling (MP4) help children conceptualize and solve addition and subtraction problems. Exercises in Lessons 3.4 and 3.6, in which children must add three addends and relate addition and subtraction, will specifically help build fluency. As children learn more strategies for adding and subtracting numbers, their fluency with both addition and subtraction strengthens.

Build fluency with associated fact fluency activities and strengthen children's proficiency with various math strategies. Use *Strategies and Practices for Skills and Fact Fluency — Primary, GK–3*: Level 3, Worksheets 2A–2B to strengthen children's mastery of addition and subtraction within 20.

Lesson 3.6 **198**

Use Ten to Subtract

LESSON AT A GLANCE

F C R Focus:

Common Core State Standard

2.OA.B.2 Fluently add and subtract within 20 using mental strategies. By end of Grade 2, know from memory all sums of two one-digit numbers.

2.MD.B.6 Represent whole numbers as lengths from 0 on a number line diagram with equally spaced points corresponding to the numbers 0, 1, 2, ..., and represent whole-number sums and differences within 100 on a number line diagram.

MATHEMATICAL PRACTICES (See *Mathematical Practices in GO Math!* in the *Planning Guide* for full text.)
MP2 Reason abstractly and quantitatively. **MP5** Use appropriate tools strategically.
MP6 Attend to precision. **MP7** Look for and make use of structure. **MP8** Look for and express regularity in repeated reasoning.

F C R Coherence:

Standards Across the Grades
Before	Grade 2	After
1.OA.A.1	2.OA.B.2	3.OA.D.8
1.OA.C.6	2.MD.B.6	

F C R Rigor:

Level 1: Understand Concepts....................*Share and Show* (✓ Checked Items)
Level 2: Procedural Skills and Fluency.......*On Your Own, Practice and Homework*
Level 3: Applications.................................*Think Smarter and Go Deeper*

Learning Objective

Find differences on a number line to develop the mental strategy of decomposing to simplify facts.

Language Objective

Children share using a sentence frame,
In my experience, getting to 10 in subtraction helps when finding differences by _____.

Materials

MathBoard

F C R For more about how *GO Math!* fosters **Coherence** within the Content Standards and Mathematical Progressions for this chapter, see page 159J.

About the Math

Professional Development

Progress to Algebra
Why Teach This?

By encouraging children to work flexibly with numbers, both their number sense and their computation skills can be strengthened.

In this lesson, children use the benchmark number 10 when finding differences for basic facts. Number lines are included in the lesson as a visual aid to reinforce this mental math strategy. This is just one of several strategies that children can use to solve basic subtraction facts. In later chapters, this strategy can be used in multi-digit subtraction problems.

 Professional Development Videos

 GO DIGITAL

 **SE** **Interactive Student Edition**

 **Personal Math Trainer**

 **Math on the Spot Video**

iT **iTools: Number Lines**

Problem of the Day 3.7

Basic Facts **Complete the subtraction sentences.**

10 − 3 = _____ 7

10 − 5 = _____ 5

10 − 1 = _____ 9

Vocabulary

Vocabulary Builder
Differences and Sums

Review differences and sums with children by asking them to complete tasks such as the following:

- **Write a number sentence in which the difference is 5.** Possible answer: 8 − 3 = 5

- **Write a number sentence in which the sum is 8.** Possible answer: 5 + 3 = 8

Literature Connection

From the Grab-and-Go™ Differentiated Centers Kit

Children read the book and find how two bears share 16 blueberries.

Benny, Bessie, and the Blueberries

① ENGAGE

with the Interactive Student Edition

Essential Question

How does getting to 10 in subtraction help when finding differences?

Making Connections

Review with the children how to make a ten to add.

What numbers added together make 10? Answers will vary.
How do we make a ten when adding? Answers will vary.
Would it also be helpful to make a ten in subtraction? In what way? Answers will vary.

Learning Activity

What is the problem the children are trying to solve?

- **How many rocks does Jessie need to collect?** 15 rocks

- **How many rocks has he already collected?** 8 rocks

- **What operation can we use to find the number of rocks he still needs to collect?** subtraction

- **Counting up is one way to solve the problem, but what is another way?** Answers will vary.

Literacy and Mathematics

Choose one or more of the following activities.

- Ask children to explain in words how making a10 helps with subtraction.

- Talk with the children about the words *more* and *less* and how they relate to operations in math. For example, if Tom has 5 more crayons than Sally and Sally has 6 crayons, what operation is used to find the number of crayons that Tom has?

2 EXPLORE

Listen and Draw

Common Core **MATHEMATICAL PRACTICES**

MP5 Use appropriate tools strategically. Read the following problem aloud.

Deveron has 13 crayons. He gives 3 crayons to Tyler. How many crayons does Deveron have now?

- **Will you add or subtract to solve?** subtract

Have children circle the part of the blue line segment on the first number line to show what is subtracted from 13.

- **What is the difference?** 10 crayons

Then read the following problem aloud.

Diane has 17 crayons. She gives 7 crayons to Anthony. How many crayons does Diane have now?

Guide a similar discussion about this problem. Have children circle the part of the blue line segment on the second number line to show what is subtracted from 17.

Then read this final problem aloud.

James has 12 crayons. He gives 2 crayons to Cassie. How many crayons does James have now?

Discuss this problem. Have children circle the part of the blue line segment on the third number line to show what is subtracted from 12.

 MP7 Look for and make use of structure. Use Math Talk to focus on children's understanding of what is subtracted from a teens number to get to 10.

ELL **Strategy:**
Model Concepts

Model 13 − 7 to help children understand how to use 10 in subtraction.

- **Draw a number line with numbers 1 to 13 on the board. Have 13 children stand under the number line so that each child represents 1 number.**

- **Ask: How many do we need to subtract from 13 to get to 10?** 3 **Have 3 children sit down.**

- **Explain that now you need to subtract 4 from 10. Have 4 more children sit down.**

- **Ask: How many children are still standing?** 6

Progress to Algebra

2.OA.B.2 Fluently add and subtract within 20 using mental strategies. By end of Grade 2, know from memory all sums of two one-digit numbers.
2.MD.B.6 Represent whole numbers as lengths from 0 on a number line diagram with equally spaced points corresponding to the numbers 0, 1, 2, ..., and represent whole-number sums and differences within 100 on a number line diagram.

Name _____

Lesson 3.7

Use Ten to Subtract

Essential Question How does getting to 10 in subtraction help when finding differences?

 Common Core **Operations and Algebraic Thinking—2.OA.B.2** *Also 2.MD.B.6*
MATHEMATICAL PRACTICES
MP5, MP7, MP8

Listen and Draw

Problem Type:
Take From • Result Unknown

Circle to show the amount you subtract for each problem.

Check children's work.

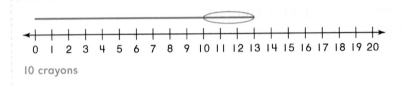

10 crayons

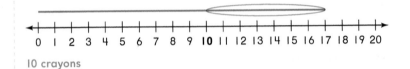

10 crayons

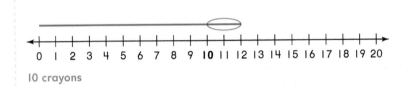

10 crayons

Math Talk: Possible answer: For each problem, the number of crayons left over is 10. The ones digit in each number we started with is how many were subtracted.

 Math Talk MATHEMATICAL PRACTICES 7

Look for Structure Describe a pattern in the three problems and answers.

© Houghton Mifflin Harcourt Publishing Company

FOR THE TEACHER • Read the following problem. Deveron has 13 crayons. He gives 3 crayons to Tyler. How many crayons does Deveron have now? Have children circle the part of the blue line segment that shows what is subtracted from the total. Repeat for two more problems.

Chapter 3

one hundred ninety-nine **199**

Reteach 3.7 ▲ **RtI**

Lesson 3.7
Reteach

Name _____

Use Ten to Subtract

You can get to ten to help find differences.
13 − 7 = **?**

Step ① Start with the first number.

Step ② Subtract ones to get to 10.

⊙⊙⊙⊙⊙⊙⊙⊙⊙⊙⊙⊙⊙

13 − 3 = 10

Step ③ Subtract the rest from the 10.

Think: I had 7. I subtracted 3 to get to 10. Now I subtract the 4 I have left.

10 − **4** = **6**

Step ④ Write the difference.

13 − 7 = **6**

Show the tens fact you used. Write the difference.

1. 15 − 8 = **7**
   5 3
   10 − **3** = **7**

2. 12 − 4 = **8**
   2 2
   10 − **2** = **8**

3. 11 − 7 = **4**
   10 − **6** = **4**

4. 13 − 5 = **8**
   10 − **2** = **8**

Chapter Resources
© Houghton Mifflin Harcourt Publishing Company
3-17
Reteach

Enrich 3.7

Differentiated Instruction

Lesson 3.7
Enrich

Name _____

Create a Subtraction Problem

Write a number from the circle in the first box. Write a number from the square in the second box. Use each number only once. Then solve.

11 12
13 14

6
5 8
7

Answers will vary. Check children's work.

1. There were ☐ ducks at the pond. ☐ ducks flew away. How many ducks are at the pond now?

   _____ − _____ = _____

2. Roberto found ☐ shells at the beach. He gave ☐ shells to his sister. How many shells does Roberto have now?

   _____ − _____ = _____

3. There are ☐ flowers in the garden. ☐ flowers are pink. The other flowers are yellow. How many flowers are yellow?

   _____ − _____ = _____

4. Anna cut out ☐ shapes. ☐ shapes are round. The other shapes are square. How many shapes are square?

   _____ − _____ = _____

 Writing and Reasoning How could you use a tens fact to solve Exercise 4?

Children's answers should demonstrate understanding of how to use a tens fact to subtract.

Chapter Resources
© Houghton Mifflin Harcourt Publishing Company
3-18
Enrich

Model and Draw

You can subtract in steps to use a tens fact.

$$14 - 6 = ?$$
       4   2

Subtract in steps:
14 − 4 = 10
10 − 2 = 8

−2   −4

0 1 2 3 4 5 6 7 8 9 10 11 12 13 14 15 16 17 18 19 20

So, $14 - 6 = \underline{8}$.

Share and Show

Show the tens fact you used. Write the difference.

0 1 2 3 4 5 6 7 8 9 10 11 12 13 14 15 16 17 18 19 20

1. $12 - 5 = \underline{7}$
         2 3
   $10 - \underline{3} = \underline{7}$

2. $11 - 6 = \underline{5}$
         1 5
   $10 - \underline{5} = \underline{5}$

3. $15 - 7 = \underline{8}$

   $10 - \underline{2} = \underline{8}$

4. $13 - 7 = \underline{6}$

   $10 - \underline{4} = \underline{6}$

200 two hundred

Advanced Learners
 Kinesthetic / Interpersonal Partners

Materials index cards

- Make two sets of index cards with subtraction expressions written on them. Set 1 has expressions with 10 as the minuend. Set 2 has a teen number as the minuend. Each card in Set 1 has the same difference as one card in Set 2.

  | $10 - 2$ | $14 - 6$ |

- Give pairs of children both sets of cards. Have them shuffle all the cards and place them facedown in rows and columns.

- Have children play a matching game in which they turn over two cards at a time and try to find pairs of cards with the same difference.

Model and Draw  MATHEMATICAL PRACTICES

MP2 Reason abstractly and quantitatively. Work through the model with children. Discuss with children what a tens fact is. Point out that by subtracting 4 and then 2, they subtract a total of 6 from 14.

- **Why is 6 broken apart as 4 and 2?**
  Possible answer: To get to 10, we need to subtract 4 from 14. 4 + 2 = 6, so we need to subtract 2 more.

③ EXPLAIN

Share and Show

Connect Exercises 1–4 to the learning model.

Have children first find what they need to subtract to get to 10 and then show the tens fact they used to find the difference.

- **In Exercise 1, how did you find the tens fact to use for the problem?** Possible answer: I subtract 2 from 12 to get to 10. I need to subtract 3 more to subtract 5 in all, so I use the tens fact 10 − 3 = 7.

Use the checked exercises for **Quick Check.** Children should use their MathBoards to show their solutions to these exercises.

✓ Quick Check

If → a child misses the checked exercises

Then → **Differentiate Instruction with**
- Reteach 3.7
- Personal Math trainer 2.OA.B.2, 2.MD.B.6
- RtI Tier 1 Activity (online)

⚠ COMMON ERRORS

Error Children use the wrong tens fact.

Example In Exercise 3, children write the tens fact 10 − 5 = 5.

Springboard to Learning Have children look at the marks and the pair of numbers below the subtrahend in Exercise 1. Discuss why the number being subtracted is broken apart in this way. Have children draw marks and write pairs of numbers below the other subtrahends so that they can keep track of their work as they complete the exercises.

4 ELABORATE

On Your Own

If a child answers the checked exercises correctly, assign Exercises 5–10.

GO DEEPER

MP6 Attend to precision. To extend thinking, have children make connections between subtraction facts and tens facts. Give children a tens fact, such as 10 − 3 = 7. Ask children to work in pairs to write two subtraction sentences that they can use this tens fact to help them solve. Possible answers: 15 − 8 = ■, 12 − 5 = ■

THINK SMARTER

In Exercise 10, children use higher order thinking skills to find the number of crayons Beth has after she gives some away. Suggest that children subtract the 3 crayons that Beth gives to Jake from the number she started with. Then subtract the 7 crayons that Beth gives to Wendy from the difference above.

Math on the Spot Video Tutor

Use this video to help children model and solve this type of *Think Smarter* problem.

GO DIGITAL **Math on the Spot** videos are in the Interactive Student Edition and at *www.thinkcentral.com*.

Additional Example

Take From • Start Unknown

- **A plant nursery sells 18 rose bushes one day. At the end of the day, 7 rose bushes are left. How many rose bushes did the nursery have at the beginning of the day?** 25 rose bushes

---

Name _____

On Your Own

Show the tens fact you used. Write the difference.

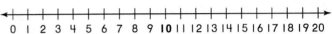

0 1 2 3 4 5 6 7 8 9 **10** 11 12 13 14 15 16 17 18 19 20

5. 13 − 5 = __8__

10 − __2__ = __8__

6. 15 − 6 = __9__

10 − __1__ = __9__

7. 12 − 8 = __4__

10 − __6__ = __4__

8. 14 − 8 = __6__

10 − __4__ = __6__

9. **GO DEEPER** Chris had 15 stickers. He gave Ann and Suzy each the same number of stickers. Now Chris has 7 stickers. How many stickers did he give to each girl?

__4__ stickers

Solve. Write or draw to explain.

10. **THINK SMARTER** Beth has a box of 16 crayons. She gives 3 crayons to Jake and 7 crayons to Wendy. How many crayons does Beth have now?

__6__ crayons

Chapter 3 • Lesson 7   two hundred one **201**

PROBLEM TYPE SITUATIONS

Addition and Subtraction

Take From • Result Unknown
Exercise: 10

Take From • Change Unknown
Exercise: 9

Problem Solving • Applications

 WRITE ▸ Math

GO DEEPER Write number sentences that use both addition and subtraction. Use each choice only once. *Order of answers may vary.*

11.
$$9 - 2 = 3 + 4$$
$$7 \quad = \quad 7$$

12.
$$1 + 4 = 10 - 5$$

13.
$$14 - 6 = 4 + 4$$

14.
$$5 + 4 = 15 - 6$$

15. THINK SMARTER Does the number sentence have the same difference as $15 - 7 = \blacksquare$? Choose Yes or No.

$10 - 6 = \blacksquare$ ○ Yes ● No

$10 - 2 = \blacksquare$ ● Yes ○ No

$10 - 4 = \blacksquare$ ○ Yes ● No

 TAKE HOME ACTIVITY • Ask your child to name pairs of numbers that have a difference of 10. Then have him or her write the number sentences.

© Houghton Mifflin Harcourt Publishing Company

Choices box:
~~9 − 2~~
~~3 + 4~~
1 + 4
14 − 6
5 + 4
15 − 6
10 − 5
4 + 4

Problem Solving • Applications   Real World

GO DEEPER

MP8 Look for and express regularity in repeated reasoning. Exercises 11–14 require children to use higher order thinking skills to find both an addition and a subtraction expression with the same value. Guide children through Exercise 11 and then discuss strategies children might use to complete the other three number sentences.

THINK SMARTER

Children may not recognize that only the second equation demonstrates the correct use of a tens fact to find the difference.

5 EVALUATE Formative Assessment

Essential Question

Reflect Using the Language Objective Have children complete the sentence frame, In my experience, getting to 10 in subtraction helps when finding differences by _____, to answer the Essential Question.

How does getting to 10 in subtraction help when finding differences? Possible answer: If I get to 10, then I can use a tens fact to find the difference.

Math Journal WRITE ▸ Math

Describe how to use a tens fact to find the difference for $15 - 8$.

DIFFERENTIATED INSTRUCTION INDEPENDENT ACTIVITIES

Differentiated Centers Kit

Activities
A Heap of Sheep

Children complete orange Activity Card 3 by solving a two-part subtraction problem using numbers through 18.

Literature
Benny, Bessie, and the Blueberries

Children read the book and find how two bears share 16 blueberries.

Games
On the Ferris Wheel

Games

Children practice basic subtraction facts to move along the game path.

Practice and Homework

Use the Practice and Homework pages to provide children with more practice of the concepts and skills presented in this lesson. Children master their understanding as they complete practice items and then challenge their critical thinking skills with Problem Solving. Use the Write Math section to determine children's understanding of content for this lesson. Encourage children to use their Math Journals to record their answers.

Name _____

Use Ten to Subtract

Common Core COMMON CORE STANDARD—2.OA.B.2
Add and subtract within 20.

Show the tens fact you used.
Write the difference.

1. $14 - 6 = \underline{8}$

   $10 - \underline{2} = \underline{8}$

2. $12 - 7 = \underline{5}$

   $10 - \underline{5} = \underline{5}$

3. $13 - 7 = \underline{6}$

   $10 - \underline{4} = \underline{6}$

4. $15 - 8 = \underline{7}$

   $10 - \underline{3} = \underline{7}$

Problem Solving (Real World)

Solve. Write or draw to explain.

5. Carl read 15 pages on Monday night and 9 pages on Tuesday night. How many more pages did he read on Monday night than on Tuesday night?

   $\underline{6}$ more pages

6. **WRITE** Math Describe how to use a tens fact to find the difference for $15 - 8$.

   _____

   Check children's work.

© Houghton Mifflin Harcourt Publishing Company

Chapter 3   two hundred three **203**

Common Core **PROFESSIONAL DEVELOPMENT** Math Talk in Action

The class is discussing Exercise 2.

Teacher: What is the first thing you need to decide when you use a tens fact to help subtract 7 from 12?

Ahlyza: I need to find a number to subtract from 12 to get to 10.

Teacher: How do you decide what number to subtract from 12?

Matthew: I think of a number line. I know I need to jump back 2 to go from 12 to 10, so I need to subtract 2.

Natalie: I use patterns. I know that the ones digit in 12 is 2, so if I subtract 2, I will end up with 10.

Teacher: Those are both good ways to determine the number. What do you do after you subtract 2 from 12?

Damond: I know I have to subtract 7 in all. I have already subtracted 2, so I have to subtract 5 more. Since I am now subtracting from 10, I can use a tens fact, $10 - 5 = 5$.

Ahlyza: Right! Since I know that $10 - 5 = 5$, I know that $12 - 7 = 5$.

Teacher: How can you check that you subtracted correctly?

Damond: I make sure the numbers I subtracted have a sum of 7: $5 + 2 = 7$, so I subtracted the right amount.

Lesson Check (2.OA.B.2)

1. Show the tens fact you used. Write the difference.

$12 - 6 = \underline{6}$

$10 - 4 = \underline{6}$

2. Show the tens fact you used. Write the difference.

$13 - 8 = \underline{5}$

$10 - 5 = \underline{5}$

Spiral Review (2.OA.B.2, 2.NBT.A.4)

3. Write a related subtraction fact for $7 + 3 = 10$.

Possible answer:

$\underline{10 - 3 = 7}$

4. Joe has 8 trucks. Carmen has 1 more truck than Joe. How many trucks do they have now?

$\underline{17}$ trucks

5. There were 276 people on an airplane. Write a number greater than 276.

Possible answer: $\underline{279}$

6. Write $>$, $<$, or $=$ to compare.

$537 \underline{>} 375$

 FOR MORE PRACTICE
GO TO THE
Personal Math Trainer

Continue concepts and skills practice with Lesson Check. Use Spiral Review to engage children in previously taught concepts and to promote content retention. Common Core standards are correlated to each section.

Algebra • Use Drawings to Represent Problems

FOCUS   COHERENCE   RIGOR — LESSON AT A GLANCE

F C R Focus:

Common Core State Standard

2.OA.A.1 Use addition and subtraction within 100 to solve one- and two-step word problems involving situations of adding to, taking from, putting together, taking apart, and comparing, with unknowns in all positions, e.g., by using drawings and equations with a symbol for the unknown number to represent the problem.

MATHEMATICAL PRACTICES (See *Mathematical Practices in GO Math!* in the *Planning Guide* for full text.)
MP1 Make sense of problems and persevere in solving them. **MP3** Construct viable arguments and critique the reasoning of others. **MP4** Model with mathematics. **MP5** Use appropriate tools strategically. **MP6** Attend to precision.

F C R Coherence:

Standards Across the Grades

Before	Grade 2	After
1.OA.C.6	2.OA.A.1	3.OA.D.8
1.OA.A.1		
1.OA.C.5		

F C R Rigor:

Level 1: Understand Concepts....................*Share and Show* (✓ Checked Items)
Level 2: Procedural Skills and Fluency.......*On Your Own, Practice and Homework*
Level 3: Applications..................................*Think Smarter and Go Deeper*

Learning Objective
Use bar models to represent a variety of addition and subtraction situations.

Language Objective
Children create a bar model to show an addition and a subtraction problem.

Materials
MathBoard

F C R For more about how *GO Math!* fosters **Coherence** within the Content Standards and Mathematical Progressions for this chapter, see page 159J.

About the Math
Professional Development

Progress to Algebra
Using Bar Models for Comparison Subtraction

For comparison subtraction problems, two rows of bars are drawn. The top bar shows the larger amount in the comparison. The bottom bar shows the smaller amount. The bracketed area shows the unknown.

The bottom diagram shows a bar model for this comparison subtraction problem.

Emily buys 15 pears and 9 apples. How many more pears than apples does she buy?

• The larger amount is 15 pears and the smaller amount is 9 apples. So, children would subtract to find how many more pears than apples there are: $15 - 9 = 6$.

 Professional Development Videos

larger amount

smaller amount

difference

15

9

6

Daily Routines

Common Core

 **Problem of the Day 3.8**

Basic Facts

Write a subtraction fact using these three numbers. Then write a related addition fact.

| 5 | 9 | 14 |

Children may use their MathBoards to write the related number sentences.

If time permits, ask them to write a subtraction fact and a related addition fact for the numbers 7, 7, 14.

Vocabulary

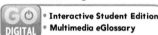 • Interactive Student Edition
• Multimedia eGlossary

Fluency Task

Read these subtraction expressions aloud to the class. Have them raise their hands when they have the answer. For each fact, invite a child to explain how they found the difference.

- 10 − 7
- 8 − 2
- 15 − 5
- 12 − 6
- 13 − 8

① ENGAGE

with the Interactive Student Edition

Essential Question

How are bar models used to show addition and subtraction problems?

Making Connections

Ask children to discuss addition, subtraction, and the ways they can be represented.

What are some ways you can show a subtraction fact? Sample answers: drawing a picture, using connecting cubes, with numbers **How did you use bar models in previous lessons?** Sample answer: I used them to show taking away and subtraction facts.

Learning Activity

What is the problem the children are trying to solve? Connect the story to the problem. Ask the following questions.

- **How can you draw a bar model to show the problem Jessie is trying to solve?** See children's work.
- **What is Jessie trying to find?** See children's work.

Literacy and Mathematics

View the lesson opener with the children. Then, choose one or more of the following activities:

- Have children write a story problem that requires subtraction. Have them circle the numbers in the subtraction fact using a blue crayon.
- Have children use connecting cubes to show the number 12. Then have them experiment in ways to break it apart. They should write each subtraction fact they find and the related subtraction and addition facts.

2 EXPLORE

Listen and Draw Real World

Common Core **MATHEMATICAL PRACTICES**

MP4 Model with mathematics. Read this problem. Have children complete the first bar model to show the problem. Then have children write the number sentence to solve.

Hailey has 5 pennies in her pocket and 7 pennies in her wallet. How many pennies does she have?

- **What did you write in the two bars? Explain.** Possible answer: I wrote 5 and 7 because these bars show the two parts being combined.

- **What did you write below the bracket? Explain.** Possible answer: I wrote 12 because 12 pennies is the whole when I combine 5 pennies and 7 pennies.

- **What number sentence did you write? Explain.** Possible answer: I wrote 5 + 7 = 12 to show that the parts are added together.

Repeat the activity for this problem. Have children complete the second bar model.

Blake has 12 pennies in his bank. He gives 5 pennies to his sister. How many pennies does he have now?

- **Why do the bar models for the two problems look the same?** Possible answer: The problems are related addition and subtraction problems. They have the same parts and the same whole.

 **MP6 Attend to precision.** Use Math Talk to focus on children's understanding of how addition and subtraction situations compare.

ELL **Strategy:**
Understand Context

Children need to experience vocabulary in context to clarify the meaning of words.

- **Write the following problem on the board and then read it aloud.**
  Sara ate 6 grapes. Jake ate 4 grapes. How many more grapes did Sara eat than Jake?

- **Discuss that the phrase** *how many* **more indicates they are comparing and that they can subtract to solve the problem. Then have children write a number sentence to solve.**

Progress to Algebra — **2.OA.A.1** Use addition and subtraction within 100 to solve one- and two-step word problems involving situations of adding to, taking from, putting together, taking apart, and comparing, with unknowns in all positions, e.g., by using drawings and equations with a symbol for the unknown number to represent the problem.

Name _____

Algebra • Use Drawings to Represent Problems

 Common Core **Operations and Algebraic Thinking—2.OA.A.1**
MATHEMATICAL PRACTICES
MP1, MP4, MP6

Essential Question How are bar models used to show addition and subtraction problems?

Listen and Draw Real World

Complete the bar model to show the problem.
Complete the number sentence to solve.

| 5 | 7 |

12

Problem Type:
Put Together/Take Apart • Total Unknown

__5__ + __7__ = __12__   __12__ pennies

| 5 | 7 |

12   Problem Type:
Take From • Result Unknown

__12__ − __5__ = __7__   __7__ pennies

 Math Talk: Possible answer: The bar models are the same. In the first problem, I solved for the whole, and in the second problem, I solved for a part.

FOR THE TEACHER • Read each problem and have children complete the bar models. Hailey has 5 pennies in her pocket and 7 pennies in her wallet. How many pennies does she have? Blake has 12 pennies in his bank. He gives 5 pennies to his sister. How many pennies does he have now?

 Math Talk MATHEMATICAL PRACTICES 6

Explain how the problems are alike and how they are different.

Chapter 3   two hundred five **205**

© Houghton Mifflin Harcourt Publishing Company

Reteach 3.8 ▲ **RtI**

Name _____

Algebra • Use Drawings to Represent Problems

You can use bar models to show problems.

There are 5 girls and 11 boys at the park. How many more boys than girls are at the park?

How many boys? → | 11 |

How many girls? → | 5 |
                      6

Write a number sentence. 11 − 5 = 6

There are 6 more boys than girls.

Complete the bar model. Then write a number sentence to solve.

1. Nathan had 7 stamps. Then he got 9 more stamps. How many stamps does Nathan have now?

| 7 | 9 |
    16

7 + 9 = 16   16 stamps

Enrich 3.8 **Differentiated Instruction**

Name _____

Picture It

Fill in a missing number that makes sense. Draw a picture and solve. Answers will vary. Check children's work.

1. Alexia had 14 marbles. She gave _____ marbles to Sam. How many marbles does Alexia have now?

_____ marbles

2. Jennifer has 7 red marbles and _____ blue marbles. How many marbles does she have?

_____ marbles

3. Carter had _____ marbles. He gave all the marbles to his brother. How many marbles does Carter have now?

0 marbles

Writing and Reasoning Explain how drawing a picture can help you solve a problem.

Possible answer: Drawing a picture shows me what is happening in a problem.

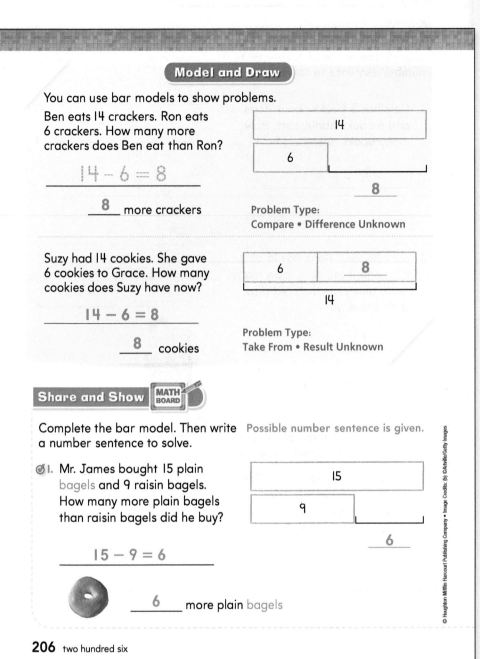

Model and Draw

You can use bar models to show problems.

Ben eats 14 crackers. Ron eats 6 crackers. How many more crackers does Ben eat than Ron?

| 14 |
| 6 |

8

$14 - 6 = 8$

____8____ more crackers

Problem Type:
Compare • Difference Unknown

Suzy had 14 cookies. She gave 6 cookies to Grace. How many cookies does Suzy have now?

| 6 | 8 |

14

$14 - 6 = 8$

____8____ cookies

Problem Type:
Take From • Result Unknown

Share and Show

Complete the bar model. Then write a number sentence to solve.

Possible number sentence is given.

☑ 1. Mr. James bought 15 plain bagels and 9 raisin bagels. How many more plain bagels than raisin bagels did he buy?

| 15 |
| 9 |

6

$15 - 9 = 6$

 ____6____ more plain bagels

Advanced Learners 🕐 Visual / Individual / Partners

Materials Addition Fact Cards, Subtraction Fact Cards (see *eTeacher Resources*)

• Have each child choose a fact card and write a word problem for the fact.

| 15 |
| − 6 |

Cara saw 15 birds in the tree. 6 birds flew away. How many birds were left?

• Have partners solve each other's problems and then write another problem using the partner's fact card.

• Repeat with other fact cards. Have partners use both addition and subtraction cards during the activity.

Model and Draw  Common Core **MATHEMATICAL PRACTICES**

MP1 Make sense of problems and persevere in solving them. Work through the models with children. Have volunteers restate the two subtraction problems in their own words. Discuss that the first problem is a comparison subtraction problem and the second problem is a take-away subtraction problem.

• **How are the two subtraction problems different?** Possible answer: In the first problem, two groups of crackers are being compared. In the second problem, 6 cookies are taken away from 14 cookies.

❸ EXPLAIN

Share and Show

Connect Exercise 1 to the learning model.

• **In Exercise 1, how did you decide how to complete the bar model?** Possible answer: I wrote 6 under the bracket since the bar model shows that Mr. James bought 6 fewer raisin bagels than plain bagels.

Use the checked exercises for Quick Check. Children should use their MathBoards to show their solution to this exercise.

✓ **Quick Check** **RtI**

If ➤ a child misses the checked exercise

Then ➤ Differentiate Instruction with
  • Reteach 3.8
  • Personal Math trainer 2.OA.A.1
  • RtI Tier 1 Activity (online)

⚠ **COMMON ERRORS**

Error Children do not understand the bar model for a comparison subtraction problem.

Example Children incorrectly label the bar model in Exercise 1.

Springboard to Learning Children may not understand the representation found in a comparison bar model. Explain that you need two bars, one for each amount. The two bars are lined up so you can see how they compare. You may want to ask children to use trains of connecting cubes to model the comparison in a more concrete way.

ELABORATE

On Your Own

If a child answers the checked exercises correctly, assign Exercises 2–4.

 THINK SMARTER

This problem assesses children's ability to represent a comparison subtraction problem with a bar model. Ask children to explain how they solve the problem step by step.

 Math on the Spot Video Tutor

Use this video to help children model and solve this type of *Think Smarter* problem.

GO DIGITAL **Math on the Spot** videos are in the Interactive Student Edition and at *www.thinkcentral.com*.

GO DEEPER

MP3 Construct viable arguments and critique the reasoning of others. Write a subtraction fact on the board.

$$14 - 6 = \square$$

First ask children to tell or write take-away subtraction story problems that could be solved by using the fact. Then ask them to tell or write comparison subtraction story problems that could be solved by using the fact.

Have children work in pairs and draw bar models for their story problems. Ask children to share their bar models and explain how their models show their story problems.

Additional Example

Read children the following problem.

- **When the toy store opens, it has 53 kites. During the day, it sells 18 kites. How many kites does the store have at the end of the day?** 35 kites

Ask children to use the same numbers and change this Result Unknown problem to a Change Unknown problem. Then have them write a Start Unknown problem.

- **How are the problems alike? How are they different?** Check children's answers.

On Your Own

Complete the bar model. Then write a number sentence to solve. Possible number sentences are given.

2. Cole has 5 books about dogs and 6 books about cats. How many books does Cole have?

5	6

11

$$5 + 6 = 11$$

_____11_____ books

3. **THINK SMARTER** Anne has 16 blue clips and 9 red clips. How many more blue clips than red clips does she have?

16

9	

7

$$16 - 9 = 7$$

_____7_____ more blue clips

4. **GO DEEPER** Fill in the blank. Then label the bar model and solve.

Answers may vary. Check children's work.

Miss Gore had 18 pencils. She gave ____ pencils to Erin. How many pencils does Miss Gore have now?

_____ pencils

PROBLEM TYPE SITUATIONS

Addition and Subtraction

Put Together/Take Apart • Result Unknown
Exercises: 2, 5

Put Together/Take Apart • Addend Unknown
Exercises: 6, 7

Take From • Result Unknown
Exercise: 4

Compare • Difference Unknown
Exercises: 1, 3

Problem Solving • Applications | WRITE ▸ Math

Use the information in the table to solve. Write or draw to explain.

Jenna's Flowers	
Flowers	Number
roses	6
tulips	8
daisies	11

5. Jenna put all of the roses and all of the tulips into a vase. How many flowers did she put into the vase?

___14___ flowers

6. **THINK SMARTER** Four of the daisies are white. The other daisies are yellow. How many daisies are yellow?

___7___ yellow daisies

7. **THINK SMARTER** Rita counts 4 frogs in the grass and some other frogs in the water. There are 10 frogs in all. How many frogs are in the water? Draw a picture and write a number sentence to solve.

Check children's drawings.

Possible answer: 4 + 6 = 10

___6___ frogs are in the water.

 TAKE HOME ACTIVITY • Ask your child to describe what he or she learned in this lesson.

208 two hundred eight

© Houghton Mifflin Harcourt Publishing Company

Problem Solving • Applications

Common Core MATHEMATICAL PRACTICES

MP5 Use appropriate tools strategically. A key to solving Exercise 5 is understanding how to find the needed information in the table.

THINK SMARTER

For Exercise 6, children use information found in the table and in the problem to solve the problem.

THINK SMARTER

Children may understand that their drawing should show one group of 4 but not understand how to represent the other group. They will be able to draw a picture that correctly represents the problem situation for Exercise 7 if they understand that 10 is the whole for a number sentence. Guide children to understand that the value of the other group is an unknown addend in an addition fact or the difference in a subtraction fact.

5 EVALUATE Formative Assessment

Essential Question

Reflect Using the Language Objective Have children create a bar model to answer the Essential Question.

How are bar models used to show addition and subtraction problems?
Possible answer: Bar models show the parts and whole that I know and help me know what is missing.

Math Journal | WRITE ▸ Math

Explain how you decided how to label the bar model in Exercise 4 on page 207.

DIFFERENTIATED INSTRUCTION | INDEPENDENT ACTIVITIES

Differentiated Centers Kit

Activities	Literature	Games
Quilting Bee	**Game Time!**	**On the Ferris Wheel**

Children complete blue Activity Card 3 by subtracting numbers through 18 in multi-step problems.

Children read the book and add or subtract to find shin guards for the soccer players.

Children practice basic subtraction facts to move along the game path.

Lesson 3.8 208

Practice and Homework

Use the Practice and Homework pages to provide children with more practice of the concepts and skills presented in this lesson. Children master their understanding as they complete practice items and then challenge their critical thinking skills with Problem Solving. Use the Write Math section to determine children's understanding of content for this lesson. Encourage children to use their Math Journals to record their answers.

Algebra • Use Drawings to Represent Problems

Common Core COMMON CORE STANDARD—2.OA.A.1
Represent and solve problems involving addition and subtraction.

Complete the bar model. Then write a number sentence to solve.

Possible number sentences are given.

I. Adam had 12 trucks. He gave 4 trucks to Ed. How many trucks does Adam have now?

_8_	4

12

$12 - 4 = 8$

____8____ trucks

2. Grandma has 14 red roses and 7 pink roses. How many more red roses than pink roses does she have?

14

7

7

$14 - 7 = 7$

____7____ more red roses

3. **WRITE** ▸ Math Explain how you used the bar model in Exercise 2 to solve the problem

_____

_____

Check children's work.

© Houghton Mifflin Harcourt Publishing Company

1. Complete the bar model. Then solve. Abby has 16 grapes. Jason has 9 grapes. How many more grapes does Abby have than Jason?

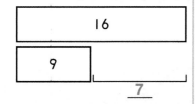

___7___ more grapes

2. Write a subtraction fact with the same difference as 16 − 7.

   Possible answer:

   ___10 − 1___

3. What is the difference?

   $18 - 9 = \underline{9}$

4. What is another way to write 300 + 20 + 5?

   ___325___

5. What is the value of the underlined digit?

   2̲8

   ___20___

FOR MORE PRACTICE
GO TO THE
Personal Math Trainer

Continue concepts and skills practice with Lesson Check. Use Spiral Review to engage children in previously taught concepts and to promote content retention. Common Core standards are correlated to each section.

Algebra • Use Equations to Represent Problems

LESSON AT A GLANCE

FOCUS **COHERENCE** **RIGOR**

F C R Focus:

Common Core State Standard

2.OA.A.1 Use addition and subtraction within 100 to solve one- and two-step word problems involving situations of adding to, taking from, putting together, taking apart, and comparing, with unknowns in all positions, e.g., by using drawings and equations with a symbol for the unknown number to represent the problem.

MATHEMATICAL PRACTICES (See *Mathematical Practices in GO Math!* in the *Planning Guide* for full text.)
MP1 Make sense of problems and persevere in solving them. **MP2** Reason abstractly and quantitatively. **MP4** Model with mathematics.

F C R Coherence:

Standards Across the Grades
Before	Grade 2	After
1.OA.C.6	2.OA.A.1	3.OA.D.8
1.OA.A.1		
1.OA.C.5		

F C R Rigor:

Level 1: Understand Concepts...................*Share and Show* (✓ Checked Items)
Level 2: Procedural Skills and Fluency.......*On Your Own, Practice and Homework*
Level 3: Applications..................................*Think Smarter and Go Deeper*

Learning Objective

Write equations to represent and solve a variety of addition and subtraction situations.

Language Objective

Child pairs discuss an example of how number sentences are used to show addition and subtraction situations.

Materials

MathBoard

F C R For more about how *GO Math!* fosters **Coherence** within the Content Standards and Mathematical Progressions for this chapter, see page 159J.

About the Math

Professional Development

MP2 Reason abstractly and quantitatively.

In this lesson, children use number sentences to represent problem situations. Children must make sense of the problem situation to understand what is happening. They assess the information given, determine what question is to be answered, and choose the operation or process to use to solve the problem.

Then children must represent the problem symbolically. One way to represent a problem is to write a number sentence. A number sentence organizes the problem situation in a mathematical way. Children complete the computation and find a solution. They should then revisit the problem and make sure they understand what their mathematical answer represents within the problem. It is important to follow these steps, reasoning both abstractly and quantitatively to solve problems.

 Professional Development Videos

GO DIGITAL

SE Interactive Student Edition

 Personal Math Trainer

 Math on the Spot Video

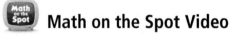 Animated Math Models

*i*T *i*Tools: Counters

 HMH Mega Math

Daily Routines

Common Core

 Problem of the Day 3.9

Basic Facts **Find each difference.**

$15 - 7 =$ _____ 8

$14 - 8 =$ _____ 6

$13 - 6 =$ _____ 7

Ask children to write three other subtraction facts that also have differences of 8, 6, and 7.

Vocabulary

GO DIGITAL • Interactive Student Edition
• Multimedia eGlossary

Fluency Task

Materials: connecting cubes

Have children use two colors of connecting cubes to represent the subtraction fact $10 - 4 = 6$. Then have children write the related addition and subtraction facts. Repeat with other subtraction facts as time allows.

① ENGAGE

with the Interactive Student Edition

Essential Question

How are number sentences used to show addition and subtraction situations?

Making Connections

Encourage children to think about problem solving.

What models can you use to show addition and subtraction problems? Answers will vary. **What words in a problem tell you to add? Subtract?** Answers will vary. Possible answers: more than, less than

Learning Activity

What is the problem the children are trying to solve? Connect the problem to the story. Have children focus on what happened to the beetles.

- **How many beetles were on the log at the beginning?** 17 beetles

- **How many beetles were left on the log after some crawled away?** 9 beetles

- **What does Jessie want to find out?** How many beetles crawled away

Literacy and Mathematics

View the lesson opener with the children. Then, choose one or more of the following activities.

- Ask the children to draw a picture of a beetle and then write a story about beetles.

- Ask the children to write a list of words that would indicate addition.

- Ask the children to write a list of words that would indicate subtraction.

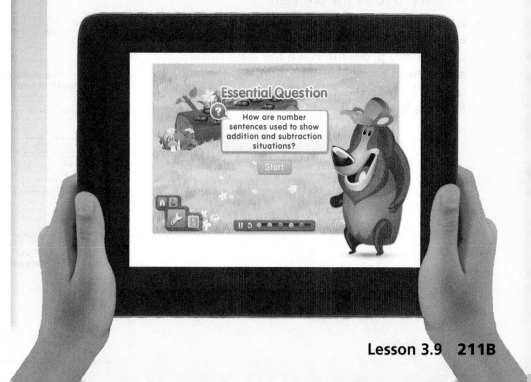

2 EXPLORE

Listen and Draw Real World

MP1 Make sense of problems and persevere in solving them. Read the directions aloud.

- **What are you asked to do?** Write a story problem that can be solved using the bar model.

- **How can you use this bar model to decide what kind of story problem to write?**
Possible answer: I can look at the bar model and know what number is the whole and what number is one part. Then I can use this information to decide if I will write an addition or a subtraction story problem.

Ask for a volunteer to read his or her story problem to the class. Ask children to describe how the bar model helps show the story problem. Then ask for additional volunteers to read their story problems and discuss them with the class.

 MP2 Reason abstractly and quantitatively. Use **Math Talk** to focus on children's understanding of how to decide whether to use addition or subtraction based on the situation.

 Strategy:

Model Concepts

Read the following problem:
There were 6 toys in a box. Some toys were taken out. There were 4 toys left in the box. How many toys were taken out? 2 toys

- **Draw a picture to model the problem to help children understand that they need to subtract to solve the problem.**

- **After children write a story problem for Listen and Draw, ask a volunteer to read his or her story problem. Have the class draw a picture to model the problem and then discuss how to use addition or subtraction to solve it.**

211 Chapter 3

Progress to Algebra

2.OA.A.1 Use addition and subtraction within 100 to solve one- and two-step word problems involving situations of adding to, taking from, putting together, taking apart, and comparing, with unknowns in all positions, e.g., by using drawings and equations with a symbol for the unknown number to represent the problem.

Name _____

Algebra • Use Equations to Represent Problems

Essential Question How are number sentences used to show addition and subtraction situations?

Lesson 3.9

Common Core **Operations and Algebraic Thinking—2.OA.A.1**
MATHEMATICAL PRACTICES
MP1, MP2, MP4

Listen and Draw  Real World

Write a story problem that could be solved using this bar model.

	9

15

Problem Type:
Add To • Start Unknown

Story problems will vary. One possible problem: Kaley had some marbles. Her brother gave her 9 more marbles. Now she has 15 marbles. How many marbles did Kaley have to start?

Math Talk: Possible answer: I would subtract. I know the total is 15 marbles, and I need to find the number of marbles that is added to 9 marbles to have 15 marbles in all.

Math Talk MATHEMATICAL PRACTICES 2

Would you add or subtract to solve your story problem? **Explain.**

FOR THE TEACHER • Discuss with children how this bar model can be used to represent an addition or a subtraction situation.

Chapter 3

two hundred eleven **211**

Differentiated Instruction

Reteach 3.9 △ RtI

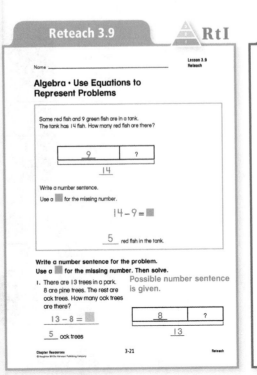

Enrich 3.9

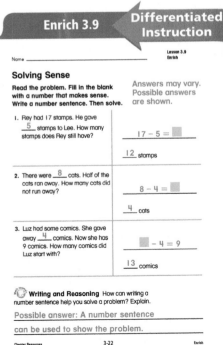

Model and Draw

A number sentence can be used to show a problem.

There were some girls and 4 boys at the park. There were 9 children in all. How many girls were at the park?

Problem Type:
Put Together/Take Apart •
Addend Unknown

 + 4 = 9

> The is a placeholder for the missing number.

Think: 5 + 4 = 9

So, there were __5__ girls at the park.

Share and Show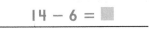

Write a number sentence for the problem.
Use a for the missing number. Then solve.

Possible number sentences are given.

✓ 1. There were 14 ants on the sidewalk. Then 6 ants went into the grass. How many ants were still on the sidewalk?

14 − 6 =

_____8_____ ants

✓ 2. There were 7 big dogs and 4 little dogs at the park. How many dogs were at the park?

7 + 4 =

_____11_____ dogs

Advanced Learners
Visual
Individual / Partners

- Ask each child to write an addition or subtraction story problem involving the number 8.

> There were 11 apples on a tree. Some apples fell off. There are 8 apples left on the tree. How many apples fell off?

- Have partners trade problems. Ask each child to draw a diagram or picture that might help him or her solve the problem.

- Have children write a number sentence that could be used to solve the problem. Then have them solve.

- Have children discuss with their partners how they solved each other's problems.

Model and Draw Common Core MATHEMATICAL PRACTICES

MP4 Model with mathematics. Work through the model with children. Explain that the gray box represents an unknown number.

- **Look at the number sentence with the gray box. How does this number sentence show the problem?** Possible answer: The gray box stands for the number of girls, and 4 is added to this amount because that is the number of boys. The sum, 9, is the number of children in all.

- **Could a subtraction sentence also be used to show the problem? Explain.** Yes; Possible answer: I could subtract 4 from 9 to find how many children are girls.

③ EXPLAIN

Share and Show

Connect Exercises 1–2 to the learning model. For some of the exercises, children may write a subtraction or an addition sentence.

- **In Exercise 1, what number sentence did you write? Explain.** Possible answer: I wrote 14 = 6 + . I know that there were 14 ants and that 6 ants left.

Use the checked exercises for **Quick Check.** Children should use their MathBoards to show their solutions to these exercises.

✓ Quick Check RtI

If → a child misses the checked exercises

Then → Differentiate Instruction with
- Reteach 3.9
- Personal Math trainer 2.OA.A.1
- RtI Tier 1 Activity (online)

⚠ COMMON ERRORS

Error Children may write an incorrect number sentence for a problem.

Example In Exercise 2, children write 7 − 4 = 3.

Springboard to Learning Have children draw a picture or diagram to model the problem. Then have children describe in their own words what the problem is about.

Lesson 3.9 212

On Your Own

If a child answers the checked exercises correctly, assign Exercises 3–6. Remind children that some of the story problems may be solved with an addition or subtraction number sentence.

Ask children to explain what each gray box in their number sentences represents in the exercises on page 213.

MP2 Reason abstractly and quantitatively.
To extend their thinking, challenge children to choose one of the exercises on this page and write a new story problem by changing the action in the story so that they would solve the problem in a different way. Encourage children to share their story problems and number sentences with the class.

This problem assesses children's ability to solve an addition problem in which the start addend is unknown. Have children explain how they wrote a number sentence before solving the problem.

**Math on the Spot
Video Tutor**
Use this video to help children model and solve this type of *Think Smarter* problem.

 Math on the Spot videos are in the Interactive Student Edition and at *www.thinkcentral.com*.

Name _____

On Your Own

Write a number sentence for the problem. Use a ▨ for the missing number. Then solve.

Possible number sentences are given.

3. A group of children were flying 13 kites. Some kites were put away. Then the children were flying 7 kites. How many kites were put away?

$$13 - \blacksquare = 7$$

_____ 6 kites

4. There are 18 boys at the field. 9 of the boys are playing soccer. How many boys are not playing soccer?

$$18 - 9 = \blacksquare$$

_____ 9 boys

5. **MATHEMATICAL PRACTICE ② Use Reasoning**
Matthew found 9 acorns. Greg found 6 acorns. How many acorns did the two boys find?

$$9 + 6 = \blacksquare$$

_____ 15 acorns

6. **THINK SMARTER** There were some ducks in a pond. Four more ducks joined them. Then there were 12 ducks in the pond. How many ducks were in the pond at first?

_____ 8 ducks

© Houghton Mifflin Harcourt Publishing Company • Image Credits: (bc) ©Juniors Bildarchiv/Alamy

---

PROBLEM TYPE SITUATIONS

Addition and Subtraction

Add To • Result Unknown
Exercise: 8

Add To • Start Unknown
Exercise: 6

Take From • Result Unknown
Exercises: 1, 9

Take From • Change Unknown
Exercise: 3

Put Together/Take Apart • Total Unknown
Exercises: 2, 5, 7

Put Together/Take Apart • Addend Unknown
Exercise: 4

Compare • Difference Unknown
Exercise: 8

Problem Solving • Applications Real World

 WRITE Math

Read the story. Write or draw to show how you solved the problems.

> At camp, 5 children are playing games and 4 children are making crafts. 5 other children are having a snack.

7. How many children are at camp?

__14__ children

8. **GO DEEPER** Suppose 7 more children arrive at camp and join the children playing games. How many more children are playing games than children not playing games?

__3__ more children

 Personal Math Trainer

9. **THINK SMARTER+** Ashley had 9 crayons. She gave 4 crayons to her brother. How many crayons does Ashley have now? Write a number sentence for the problem. Use ▨ for the missing number. Then solve.

$$9 - 4 = \blacksquare$$

Ashley has __5__ crayons now.

 TAKE HOME ACTIVITY • Ask your child to explain how he or she solved one of the problems on this page.

214 two hundred fourteen

Problem Solving • Applications Real World

Common Core MATHEMATICAL PRACTICES

GO DEEPER

MP2 Reason abstractly and quantitatively Have children read the story. Exercise 8 requires children to use higher order thinking skills to solve a multistep problem. They use information found at the top of the page and in the exercise to solve.

THINK SMARTER

Be sure to assign this exercise to children in the Personal Math Trainer. It features an animation to help them model and answer the exercise. Children may be able to translate the problem situation into an equation, and correctly complete the left side of the equation. If children do not find the correct difference, they may have difficulty recalling subtraction facts.

5 EVALUATE Formative Assessment

Essential Question

Reflect Using the Language Objective Have child pairs discuss an example to answer the Essential Question.

How are number sentences used to show addition and subtraction situations?

Possible answer: Number sentences show the parts and the whole.

Math Journal WRITE Math

Write a story problem for the addition sentence 7 + ▨ = 9. Solve the story problem.

DIFFERENTIATED INSTRUCTION INDEPENDENT ACTIVITIES

Differentiated Centers Kit

Activities
Canine Collection

Children complete purple Activity Card 3 by writing related facts using various sets of numbers.

Literature
Game Time!

Children read the book and add or subtract to find shin guards for the soccer players.

Games
On the Ferris Wheel

Games

Children practice basic subtraction facts to move along the game path.

Practice and Homework

Use the Practice and Homework pages to provide children with more practice of the concepts and skills presented in this lesson. Children master their understanding as they complete practice items and then challenge their critical thinking skills with Problem Solving. Use the Write Math section to determine children's understanding of content for this lesson. Encourage children to use their Math Journals to record their answers.

Name _____

Algebra • Use Equations to Represent Problems

 **COMMON CORE STANDARD—2.OA.A.1**
Represent and solve problems involving addition and subtraction.

Write a number sentence for the problem.
Use a ▬ for the missing number. Then solve.

Possible number sentences are given.

1. There were 15 apples in a bowl. Dan used some apples to make a pie. Now there are 7 apples in the bowl. How many apples did Dan use?

   $15 - \blacksquare = 7$

   __8__ apples

2. Amy has 16 gift bags. She fills 8 gift bags with whistles. How many gift bags are not filled with whistles?

   $16 - 8 = \blacksquare$

   __8__ gift bags

Problem Solving

Write or draw to show how you solved the problem.

3. Tony has 7 blue cubes and 6 red cubes. How many cubes does he have?

   __13__ cubes

4. **WRITE ▸ Math** Write a story problem _____
   for the addition sentence
   $7 + \blacksquare = 9$. Solve the story _____
   problem.
   _____

© Houghton Mifflin Harcourt Publishing Company

Chapter 3   two hundred fifteen **215**

Lesson Check (2.OA.A.1)

1. Fred peeled 9 carrots. Nancy peeled 6 carrots. How many fewer carrots did Nancy peel than Fred?

   __3__ fewer carrots

2. Omar has 8 marbles. Joy has 7 marbles. How many marbles do they have together?

   _15_ marbles

Spiral Review (2.OA.B.2, 2.NBT.A.1)

3. What is the sum?

   $8 + 8 =$ _16_

4. What is the sum?

   $5 + 4 + 3 =$ _12_

5. What number has the same value as 1 hundred 7 tens?

   _170_

6. What is another way to write the number 358?

   Possible answer:

   __3__ hundreds __5__ tens __8__ ones

FOR MORE PRACTICE
GO TO THE
Personal Math Trainer

© Houghton Mifflin Harcourt Publishing Company

Continue concepts and skills practice with Lesson Check. Use Spiral Review to engage children in previously taught concepts and to promote content retention. Common Core standards are correlated to each section.

Problem Solving • Equal Groups

LESSON AT A GLANCE

FOCUS COHERENCE RIGOR

F C R Focus:

Common Core State Standards

☐ **2.OA.C.4** Use addition to find the total number of objects arranged in rectangular arrays with up to 5 rows and up to 5 columns; write an equation to express the total as a sum of equal addends.

MATHEMATICAL PRACTICES (See *Mathematical Practices in GO Math!* in the *Planning Guide* for full text.)
MP1 Make sense of problems and persevere in solving them. **MP5** Use appropriate tools strategically.
MP6 Attend to precision. **MP7** Look for and make use of structure.

F C R Coherence:

Standards Across the Grades

Before	Grade 2	After
1.OA.C.6	2.OA.C.4	3.OA.A.1
1.OA.A.1		3.OA.D.8

F C R Rigor:

Level 1: Understand Concepts....................*Share and Show* (✓ Checked Items)
Level 2: Procedural Skills and Fluency.......*On Your Own, Practice and Homework*
Level 3: Applications...................................*Think Smarter and Go Deeper*

Learning Objective
Solve problems involving equal groups by using the strategy act it out.

Language Objective
Children act out a problem about equal groups and then share how it helped them solve the problem.

Materials
MathBoard, two-color counters

F C R For more about how *GO Math!* fosters **Coherence** within the Content Standards and Mathematical Progressions for this chapter, see page 159J.

About the Math

Professional Development

Acting Out Problems About Equal Groups

In this lesson, children act out problems that involve equal groups. They use objects to represent the problem situations.

Children may draw to show equal groups of objects. To show five groups of two objects, a child could draw two objects in one row, and then draw four more rows with two objects in each row. He or she could count by twos to find the total number of objects.

Acting out and solving this type of problem lets children apply their knowledge of skip counting in real-world situations. It also builds a foundation for learning about multiplication in later grades.

 Professional Development Videos

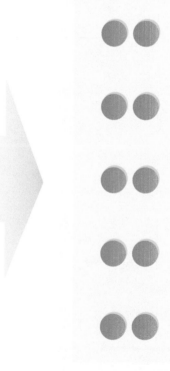

Daily Routines

Common Core

 Problem of the Day 3.10

Calendar Math **Count by fives on a calendar.**

Have children count by fives, starting with 5. Invite them to circle each number on a calendar as they count. Ask them to describe any patterns they see. Possible answer: Every fifth number is circled.

Vocabulary

 • Interactive Student Edition
• Multimedia eGlossary

Fluency Task

Read these expressions aloud to children and have them draw cubes to find the answers.

- **1 + 1 + 1**
- **2 + 2 + 2**
- **3 + 3 + 3**
- **4 + 4 + 4**
- **5 + 5 + 5**

① ENGAGE

with the Interactive Student Edition

Essential Question

How can acting it out help with solving a problem about equal groups?

Making Connections

Ask children what they know about skip counting by different numbers.

How do you skip count by 2s? Say the first five numbers you would say. Sample answer: you start with 2 and then say every other number: 2, 4, 6, 8, 10. **How do think you would skip count by 3s? Say the first five numbers you would say.** Sample answer: you start with 3 and then say every third number: 3, 6, 9, 12, 15.

Learning Activity

What is the problem the children are trying to solve? Connect the story to the problem. Ask the following questions.

- **How many equal groups are there in the problem? How many are in each group?** See children's work.

- **How can you use addition to find the total number?** Sample answer: you can add the same number together over and over to find the total.

Literacy and Mathematics

View the lesson opener with the children. Then, choose one or more of the following activities:

- Have children write a story about equal groups. Have them circle the number of groups in green and the number in the groups in blue. Ask them to guess at different ways they can find the total number.

- Have children use connecting cubes to represent 4 equal groups of 3. Have them count to find the total.

② EXPLORE

Unlock the Problem

 **MATHEMATICAL PRACTICES**

Materials two-color counters

MP5 Use appropriate tools strategically.
After reading the problem with children, work through the problem solving graphic organizer together.

- **What are you asked to find?** how many stickers Theo has

- **What information do you need to use?** He puts stickers in 5 rows. There are 3 stickers in each row.

- **How can you use the strategy** *act it out* **to solve this problem?** Possible answer: I can use counters to stand for the stickers. I can use 5 rows of counters with 3 counters in each row.

Have children use the counters to act out the problem. Have them make rows with equal groups of counters. Then have them draw a picture of their rows of counters to show their work.

- **How can skip counting help you find the solution?** Possible answer: The counters can help me skip count by threes to find the total number of stickers: 3, 6, 9, 12, 15.

Have children answer the question in the problem. Theo has 15 stickers.

 Strategy:
Illustrate Understanding

Children can demonstrate their understanding of story problems by drawing a picture.

- **Read the story problem. There are 5 flowers in each garden. How many flowers are there in 2 gardens?**

- **Have children draw to solve the story problem.**

- **Have children describe what their drawing shows.**

2.OA.C.4 Use addition to find the total number of objects arranged in rectangular arrays with up to 5 rows and up to 5 columns; write an equation to express the total as a sum of equal addends.

Name _____

Problem Solving • Equal Groups

PROBLEM SOLVING
Lesson 3.10

Essential Question How can acting it out help when solving a problem about equal groups?

Common Core **Operations and Algebraic Thinking—2.OA.C.4**
MATHEMATICAL PRACTICES
MP1, MP5, MP7

Theo puts his stickers in 5 rows.
There are 3 stickers in each row.
How many stickers does Theo have?

Problem Type:
Put Together/Take Apart • Total Unknown

Unlock the Problem

What do I need to find?

how many stickers

Theo has

What information do I need to use?

5 rows of stickers

3 stickers in each row

Show how to solve the problem.

Check children's work.

15 stickers

HOME CONNECTION • Your child used counters to act out the problem. Counters are a concrete tool that helps children act out the problem.

Chapter 3

two hundred seventeen **217**

Reteach 3.10 ▲ RtI

Name _____

Lesson 3.10
Reteach

Problem Solving • Equal Groups

Clarence puts grapes in 4 rows.
He puts 5 grapes in each row.
How many grapes does Clarence have?

Unlock the Problem

What do I need to find?	**What information do I need to use?**
how many grapes	Clarence has 4 rows of grapes.
Clarence has	He puts 5 grapes in each row.

Show how to solve the problem.

○○○○○
○○○○○
○○○○○
○○○○○

Clarence has 20 grapes.

Draw to show what you did.

1. Rachel puts her markers in 3 rows.
Each row has 3 markers.
How many markers does Rachel have?

Check children's drawings.

Rachel has 9 markers.

Chapter Resources
©Houghton Mifflin Harcourt Publishing Company

3-23

Reteach

Enrich 3.10 **Differentiated Instruction**

Name _____

Lesson 3.10
Enrich

Sorting Stickers

Jamal's stickers need to be organized. Each type of sticker must be grouped together. Different types of stickers cannot be on the same page. Each page can fit 2 rows of 3 stickers.
Draw a diagram to show the pages.

1. How many pages do you need for ♡? 1 page; Check children's work.

2. How many pages do you need for ☺? 1 page; Check children's work.

3. How many pages do you need for ☆? 3 pages; Check children's work.

4. How many pages do you need for ☽? 1 page; Check children's work.

Writing and Reasoning How many rows of 3 stickers can Jamal make in all? Write the counting pattern to show the total.

10 rows

3, 6, 9, 12, 15, 18, 21, 24, 27, 30

Chapter Resources
©Houghton Mifflin Harcourt Publishing Company

3-24

Enrich

Try Another Problem

Act out the problem.
Draw to show what you did.

> • What do I need to find?
> • What information do I need to use?

1. Maria puts all of her postcards in 4 rows. There are 3 postcards in each row. How many postcards does Maria have?

_____12_____ postcards

Check children's drawings.

2. Jamal puts 4 toys in each box. How many toys will he put in 4 boxes?

_____16_____ toys

Check children's drawings.

Math Talk: Possible answer: Acting it out helped me skip count by fours to find the total number of toys: 4, 8, 12, 16.

 Math Talk

MATHEMATICAL PRACTICES 7

Explain how acting it out and skip counting helped you solve the second problem.

© Houghton Mifflin Harcourt Publishing Company

218 two hundred eighteen

Share and Show

Connect Exercises 3–5 to the learning model.

After children solve each problem, have volunteers share their solutions with the class. Encourage them to defend their solutions. Ask questions such as the following.

- **What does your picture look like?**
- **What skip counting pattern does your picture show?**

THINK SMARTER

 Math on the Spot Video Tutor
Use this video to help children model and solve this type of *Think Smarter* problem.

 Math on the Spot videos are in the Interactive Student Edition and at *www.thinkcentral.com*.

GO DEEPER

MP7 Look for and make use of structure.
Have children each choose one problem on this page and rewrite the problem so that there is a greater number of equal groups. Then have children describe how to solve the problem.

 Quick Check ▲ **RtI**

If ▶ a child misses the checked exercises

Then ▶ **Differentiate Instruction** with
- Reteach 3.10
- Personal Math trainer 2.0A.C.4
- RtI Tier 1 Activity (online)

Name _____

Share and Show

Act out the problem.
Draw to show what you did.

☑ 3. Mr. Fulton puts 3 bananas on each tray. How many bananas are on 4 trays?

____12____ bananas

☑ 4. There are 3 rows of apples. There are 5 apples in each row. How many apples are there?

____15____ apples

5. THINK SMARTER There are 4 plates. Dexter puts 2 grapes on each plate. Then he puts 2 grapes on each of 6 more plates. How many grapes in all does he put on the plates?

____20____ grapes

PROBLEM TYPE SITUATIONS

Addition and Subtraction

Add To • Result Unknown
Exercise: 5

Put Together/Take Apart • Total Unknown
Exercises: 1, 2, 3, 4, 5, 7

Problem Solving • Applications

 WRITE Math

6. MATHEMATICAL PRACTICE 6 **Make Connections**
Angela used these counters to act out a problem.

Write a problem about equal groups that Angela could have modeled with these counters.

Check children's problems for combining equal groups

with a total of 10.

_____

7. THINK SMARTER Max and 4 friends get books from the library. Each person gets 3 books. Draw a picture to show the groups of books.

Drawing should show 5 groups (or rows) of three.

How many books did they get?

___15___ books

 TAKE HOME ACTIVITY • Ask your child to explain how he or she solved one of the problems in this lesson.

220 two hundred twenty

© Houghton Mifflin Harcourt Publishing Company

 DIFFERENTIATED INSTRUCTION **INDEPENDENT ACTIVITIES**

Differentiated Centers Kit

Activities
Way to Go!

 Children complete blue Activity Card 1 by using doubles to add.

Literature
Doubles Fun on the Farm

Children read the book and add equal groups to make doubles.

---

4 ELABORATE

Problem Solving • Applications
Common Core MATHEMATICAL PRACTICES

MP6 Attend to precision. Exercise 6 requires children to use higher order thinking skills as they write a real-life problem that can be translated to the concrete representation shown with counters.

• **How can you skip count to solve Angela's problem?** Possible answer: 5, 10

THINK SMARTER

Children will be able to draw correct pictures for Exercise 7 if they understand that the problem situation involves equal groups. Children might get the numbers of books correct, but make incorrect drawings if they do not understand how to represent the problem using a drawing.

5 EVALUATE Formative Assessment

Essential Question

Reflect Using the Language Objective Have children act out a problem and then share their experience to answer the Essential Question.

How can acting it out help when solving a problem about equal groups? Possible answer: Acting it out helps me skip count the equal groups to find the total.

Math Journal  WRITE Math

Draw 3 rows with 2 counters in each row. Write a word problem that can be acted out using these counters.

Practice and Homework

Use the Practice and Homework pages to provide children with more practice of the concepts and skills presented in this lesson. Children master their understanding as they complete practice items and then challenge their critical thinking skills with Problem Solving. Use the Write Math section to determine children's understanding of content for this lesson. Encourage children to use their Math Journals to record their answers.

Problem Solving • Equal Groups

Common Core COMMON CORE STANDARD—2.OA.C.4
Work with equal groups of objects to gain foundations for multiplication.

Act out the problem.
Draw to show what you did.

Check children's work.

1. Mr. Anderson has 4 plates of cookies. There are 5 cookies on each plate. How many cookies are there?

_20_ cookies

2. Ms. Trane puts some stickers in 3 rows. There are 2 stickers in each row. How many stickers does Ms. Trane have?

_6_ stickers

© Houghton Mifflin Harcourt Publishing Company

3. WRITE ▸ Math Draw 3 rows with 2 counters in each row. Write a word problem that can be acted out using these counters.

_____

_____

Check children's work.

Common Core PROFESSIONAL DEVELOPMENT **Math Talk in Action**

Teacher: Exercise 1 says that Mr. Anderson has 4 plates with 5 cookies on each plate. What are some ways we can use to find how many cookies there are?

Matt: We can draw a diagram. There are 5 cookies on each plate, so there are 5 in each row. There are 4 plates, so there are 4 rows. I would draw a picture like this:

Teacher: Are there any other ways to find the answer?

Anna: I would rather use blocks. I would just use a ones block for each cookie. I would put 4 rows of 5 ones blocks in each row.

Chad: I think it would be easier to just write numbers, like this: 5 + 5 + 5 + 5. That is 20.

Kaya: Or, we could just skip count by fives: 5, 10, 15, 20. There are 20 cookies in all.

Teacher: You are all correct! There are many different ways to solve a problem.

Lesson Check (2.OA.C.4)

1. Jaime puts 3 oranges on each tray. How many oranges does he put on 5 trays?

_15_ oranges

2. Maurice has 4 rows of toys with 4 toys in each row. How many toys does he have?

_16_ toys

Spiral Review (2.OA.A.1, 2.OA.B.2, 2.OA.C.3)

3. Jack has 12 pencils and 7 pens. How many more pencils than pens does he have?

_5_ pencils

4. Laura has 9 apples. Jon has 6 apples. How many apples do they have together?

_15_ apples

5. Circle the even number.

1   3   5   ⑧

6. What is the sum?

$7 + 9 = \underline{16}$

FOR MORE PRACTICE
GO TO THE
Personal Math Trainer

© Houghton Mifflin Harcourt Publishing Company

Algebra • Repeated Addition

LESSON AT A GLANCE

FOCUS   COHERENCE   RIGOR

F C R Focus:

Common Core State Standards

☐ **2.OA.C.4** Use addition to find the total number of objects arranged in rectangular arrays with up to 5 rows and up to 5 columns; write an equation to express the total as a sum of equal addends.

MATHEMATICAL PRACTICES   (See *Mathematical Practices in GO Math!* in the *Planning Guide* for full text.)
MP1 Make sense of problems and persevere in solving them. **MP2** Reason abstractly and quantitatively.
MP4 Model with mathematics. **MP6** Attend to precision.

F C R Coherence:

Standards Across the Grades

Before	Grade 2	After
1.OA.C.6	2.OA.C.4	3.OA.A.1
1.OA.A.1		3.OA.D.8

F C R Rigor:

Level 1: Understand Concepts.....................*Share and Show* (✓ Checked Items)
Level 2: Procedural Skills and Fluency.......*On Your Own, Practice and Homework*
Level 3: Applications..................................*Think Smarter and Go Deeper*

Learning Objective

Write equations using repeated addition to find the total number of objects in arrays.

Language Objective

Children use an example and explain to a partner how you can write an addition sentence for problems with equal groups.

Materials

MathBoard, two-color counters

F C R For more about how *GO Math!* fosters **Coherence** within the Content Standards and Mathematical Progressions for this chapter, see page 159J.

About the Math
Professional Development

Teaching for Depth

In this lesson, children write repeated addition sentences about a group of objects arranged in multiple rows composed of equal numbers of objects.

Guide children to first recognize that the arrangement has the same number of objects in each row. Have them describe what they see in the arrangement. They may find it helpful to count the objects in each row to better understand that it is made up of equal groups. Then have them identify how many rows of equal groups make up the arrangement.

Understanding repeated addition will help children build a foundation for learning multiplication in later grades.

 Professional Development Videos

 GO DIGITAL

 **Interactive Student Edition**

Personal Math Trainer

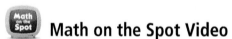 **Math on the Spot Video**

 **HMH Mega Math**

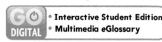 **Problem of the Day 3.11**

Word of the Day addition sentence

Use four numbers to write an example of an addition sentence. Possible answer: 3 + 4 + 5 = 12

Have children share their sentences aloud. Be sure children understand that an addition sentence must include addends, plus signs, an equal sign, and a sum.

Vocabulary

GO DIGITAL • Interactive Student Edition
• Multimedia eGlossary

Fluency Builder
Basic Facts

Common Core Fluency Standard 2.OA.B.2

Write the following problems on the board. Have children solve. Ask them to identify which facts are doubles facts.

1. $4 + 4 =$ _____ 8
2. $10 - 4 =$ _____ 6
3. $9 + 8 =$ _____ 17
4. $15 - 7 =$ _____ 8
5. $9 + 9 =$ _____ 18
6. $17 - 8 =$ _____ 9
7. $3 + 3 =$ _____ 6

Pages 122–123 in *Strategies and Practice for Skills and Facts Fluency* provide additional fluency support for this lesson.

① ENGAGE

with the Interactive Student Edition

Essential Question

How can you write an addition sentence for problems with equal groups?

Making Connections

Ask children what they know about skip counting and repeated addition.

What are the first four numbers you say when you skip count by 3s? 3, 6, 9, 12 **What are the first five numbers you say when you skip count by 4s?** 4, 8, 12, 16, 20 **How is skip counting like adding the same number over and over? Give an example.** Sample answer: when you skip count by a number it is the same as adding a number over and over; skip counting by 5s is like adding 5 over and over: 5, 10, 15, 20.

Learning Activity

What is the problem the children are trying to solve? Connect the story to the problem. Ask the following questions.

- **What are some situations in which you might use repeated addition?** Sample answer: counting the total number in equal groups.
- **How is adding 3 + 3 + 3 + 3 different than adding 3 + 3 + 3?** Sample answer: I add 3 + 3 to get 6, then 6 + 3 to get 9 for both expressions. For the first expression, I add 3 again to get 12.

Literacy and Mathematics

View the lesson opener with the children. Then, choose one or more of the following activities:

- Have children write a story problem in which they use repeated addition. Have them circle the addend they use repeatedly. Then have children trade with a partner and solve each other's problem.
- Have children use connecting cubes to represent adding a number over and over. They should make several chains of the same length to represent their addend, then count or skip count to find the total.

② EXPLORE

Listen and Draw Real World · Common Core MATHEMATICAL PRACTICES

Materials two-color counters

MP4 Model with mathematics. Read the following problem.

Clayton has 3 rows of cards. There are 5 cards in each row. How many cards does Clayton have?

Have children use counters to model the problem.

- **How many rows did you make with the counters?** 3 rows

- **Why did you place 5 counters in each row?** Possible answer: There are 5 cards in each row, so I used a counter for each card.

Have children draw a picture of their models.

- **Why is it important to draw 5 items in each row?** Possible answer: Clayton has 5 cards in each row. If I do not draw 5 items in each row, I might get the wrong answer.

- **How many cards does Clayton have?** 15 cards

 MP1 Make sense of problems and persevere in solving them.

Use **Math Talk** to focus on children's understanding of how to use models and pictures to find solutions to problems involving repeated addition.

Strategy:
Model Language

Children understand sentence structure and key phrases by listening to and repeating words and sentences modeled by the teacher.

- **Draw a row of five circles on the board. Place your finger below the first circle and move across to the fifth circle. Say the following sentence and have children repeat after you: This is one row of five objects.**

- **Have children draw 2 rows of 4 objects. Then have them describe their drawings in their own words.**

Common Core **2.0A.C.4** Use addition to find the total number of objects arranged in rectangular arrays with up to 5 rows and up to 5 columns; write an equation to express the total as a sum of equal addends.

Name _____

Lesson 3.11

Algebra • Repeated Addition
Essential Question How can you write an addition sentence for problems with equal groups?

Common Core **Operations and Algebraic Thinking—2.0A.C.4**
MATHEMATICAL PRACTICES
MP1, MP4, MP6

 Real World

Use counters to model the problem. Then draw a picture of your model.
Check children's drawings.
The answer is 15 cards.

Problem Type:
Put Together/Take Apart •
Total Unknown

Math Talk: Possible answer: I skip counted by 5 three times: 5, 10, 15. So, there are 15 counters in my model.

🍎 **FOR THE TEACHER •** Read the following problem and have children first model the problem with counters and then draw a picture of their models. Clayton has 3 rows of cards. There are 5 cards in each row. How many cards does Clayton have?

Math Talk MATHEMATICAL PRACTICES

Describe how you found the number of counters in your model.

Chapter 3

two hundred twenty-three **223**

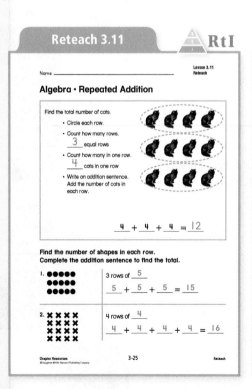

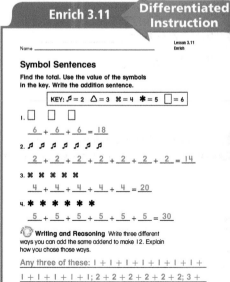

Model and Draw

You can use addition to find the total amount when you have equal groups.

3 rows of 4

Write: __4__ + __4__ + __4__ = __12__

__12__ in all

Share and Show MATH BOARD

Find the number of shapes in each row.
Complete the addition sentence to find the total.

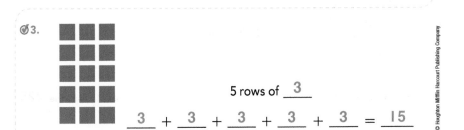

1.

3 rows of __5__

__5__ + __5__ + __5__ = __15__

⊘2.

4 rows of __4__

__4__ + __4__ + __4__ + __4__ = __16__

⊘3.

5 rows of __3__

__3__ + __3__ + __3__ + __3__ + __3__ = __15__

224 two hundred twenty-four

© Houghton Mifflin Harcourt Publishing Company

Model and Draw Common Core MATHEMATICAL PRACTICES

MP6 Attend to precision. Work through the model with children. Point out that each row has an equal number of tiles.

- **Why are there three 4s written as addends in the number sentence?** Possible answer: Each 4 stands for the four tiles in each of the three rows.

- **Why do you think the number sentence 4 + 4 + 4 = 12 is called repeated addition?** Possible answer: The number of tiles in each row is equal, so the number 4 repeats.

③ EXPLAIN

Share and Show MATH BOARD

Connect Exercises 1–3 to the learning model.

- **How did you find the total in Exercise 1?** Possible answer: I counted 5 circles in each row. I then added 5 plus 5 plus 5 to get the total of 15.

Use the checked exercises for **Quick Check**. Children should use their MathBoards to show their solutions to these exercises.

⚠ **COMMON ERRORS**

Error Children may forget to add all the numbers repeated in the addition sentence.

Example In Exercise 3, children add 3 + 3 + 3 + 3 + 3 = 12.

Springboard to Learning Have children circle the numbers as they add them and write the sum. For example, they would circle 3 + 3 and write 6. Then they would circle the next 3 and write 9. Have children continue to circle and add until they have added all the addends.

4 ELABORATE

On Your Own

If a child answers the checked exercises correctly, assign Exercises 4–8.

Go DEEPER

MP2 Reason abstractly and quantitatively.
To extend their thinking, have children write a story problem involving equal groups. Give children the following repeated addition sentence: 5 + 5 + 5 + 5 = 20. Ask them to write a story problem for the addition sentence and draw rows of equal groups to illustrate it. Have volunteers read their story problems to the class. Repeat the activity for the addition sentence 4 + 4 + 4 + 4 + 4 = 20.

Name _____

On Your Own

Find the number of shapes in each row.
Complete the addition sentence to find the total.

4.

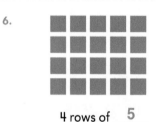

2 rows of ___4___

___4___ + ___4___ = ___8___

5.

3 rows of ___3___

___3___ + ___3___ + ___3___ = ___9___

6.

4 rows of ___5___

___5___ + ___5___ + ___5___ + ___5___ = ___20___

7.

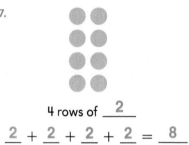

4 rows of ___2___

___2___ + ___2___ + ___2___ + ___2___ = ___8___

8.

5 rows of ___5___

___5___ + ___5___ + ___5___ + ___5___ + ___5___ = ___25___

PROBLEM TYPE SITUATION

Addition and Subtraction

Put Together/Take Apart • Total Unknown
Exercises: 9, 10

Problem Solving • Applications  WRITE Math

Solve. Write or draw to explain.

9. **THINK SMARTER** There are
6 photos on the wall. There
are 2 photos in each row.
How many rows of photos
are there?

_____3_____ rows

10. **GO DEEPER** Mrs. Chen makes
5 rows of 2 chairs and
2 rows of 3 chairs.
How many chairs does
Mrs. Chen use?

____16____ chairs

11. **THINK SMARTER** Find the number of counters in
each row. Complete the number sentence
to find the total number of counters.

__4__ + __4__ + __4__ = __12__

____12____ counters

 TAKE HOME ACTIVITY • Have your child use small objects to
make 2 rows with 4 objects in each row. Then have your child find
the total number of objects.

226 two hundred twenty-six

Problem Solving • Applications

THINK SMARTER

**MP1 Make sense of problems and
persevere in solving them.** Exercise 9
requires children to use higher order thinking
skills to find the number of rows of equal
items, instead of the number of items in all.

 ### Math on the Spot
Video Tutor
Use this video to help children model and solve
this type of _Think Smarter_ problem.

GO DIGITAL **Math on the Spot** videos are in the Interactive
Student Edition and at _www.thinkcentral.com_.

GO DEEPER

Have children read Exercise 10. Ask children
to describe how they will solve the problem.

THINK SMARTER

Children may not recognize that repeated
addition can be used for both rows and
columns in the array of objects. If they use
incorrect addends to show the correct sum,
then they likely are counting the objects
rather than understanding the concept of
repeated addition.

5 EVALUATE Formative Assessment

Essential Question

Reflect Using the Language Objective Have
children use an example and explain to a
partner to answer the Essential Question.

**How can you write an addition sentence for
problems with equal groups?** Possible answer:
I count the number of items in a row and the number
of rows. I write an addition sentence by repeating the
number of items in a row the same number of times as
there are rows.

Math Journal WRITE Math

**Explain how to write an addition sentence
for a picture of 4 rows with 3 items in
each row.**

 ## DIFFERENTIATED INSTRUCTION INDEPENDENT ACTIVITIES

Differentiated Centers Kit

**Activities
Lucy Goosey**

 Children
complete
purple Activity
Card 1 by using
manipulatives
to solve a series of addition
problems involving a growing
pattern.

**Literature
Doubles Fun on the Farm**

 Children read
the book
and add equal
groups to make
doubles.

Practice and Homework

Use the Practice and Homework pages to provide children with more practice of the concepts and skills presented in this lesson. Children master their understanding as they complete practice items and then challenge their critical thinking skills with Problem Solving. Use the Write Math section to determine children's understanding of content for this lesson. Encourage children to use their Math Journals to record their answers.

Algebra • Repeated Addition

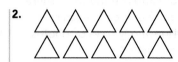

COMMON CORE STANDARD—2.OA.C.4
Work with equal groups of objects to gain foundations for multiplication.

Find the number of shapes in each row. Complete the addition sentence to find the total.

1.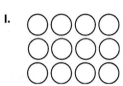

3 rows of __4__

__4__ + __4__ + __4__ = __12__

2.

2 rows of __5__

__5__ + __5__ = __10__

Problem Solving

Solve. Write or draw to explain.

3. A classroom has 3 rows of desks. There are 5 desks in each row. How many desks are there altogether?

__15__ desks

4. **WRITE** Math Explain how to write an addition sentence for a picture of 4 rows with 3 items in each row.

_____

_____

Check children's work.

Lesson Check (2.OA.C.4)

1. A scrapbook has 4 pages. There are 2 stickers on each page. How many stickers are there?

_____8_____ stickers

2. Ben makes 5 rows of coins. He puts 3 coins in each row. How many coins are there?

_____15_____ coins

Spiral Review (2.OA.B.2, 2.NBT.A.2, 2.NBT.A.3)

3. There are 5 apples and 4 oranges. How many pieces of fruit are there?

_____9_____ pieces

4. Count by tens.

40, __50__, __60__, __70__, __80__

5. Write the number 260 using words.

_____two hundred sixty_____

6. Write a fact with the same sum as 7 + 5.

Possible answer: ___10 + 2___

FOR MORE PRACTICE
GO TO THE
Personal Math Trainer

© Houghton Mifflin Harcourt Publishing Company

228 two hundred twenty-eight

Monitoring Common Core Success

Maintaining Focus on the Major Work

Part of the major work in Grade 2 is addition and subtraction within 20 (2.OA.B) and representing and solving problems involving addition and subtraction within 100 (2.OA.A). In Lessons 3.7–3.11, children learn numerous addition and subtraction problem-solving strategies such as using the benchmark number 10 to find differences for basic facts, using bar models to show addition and subtraction problems, and writing repeated addition sentences to find the total number of objects arranged in rectangular arrays.

Connecting Content Across Domains and Clusters

Within Domain 2.OA, Operations and Algebraic Thinking, children work in three different clusters, 2.OA.A, 2.OA.B, and 2.OA.C. When children use tens facts to solve subtraction problems, this work connects to solving one- and two-step problems involving addition and subtraction (2.OA.A) using bar models and number sentences. Work within this cluster is directly linked to work in Cluster 2.OA.C in which children work with equal groups and build arrays to gain foundations for multiplication.

Building Fluency

In Lessons 3.7–3.10, children work toward achieving fluency in addition and subtraction within 100 (2.OA.B.2 and 2.NBT.B.5). Exercises involving the use of drawings and equations in order to solve problems help children build fluency in addition and subtraction. The problems in Lesson 3.11, where they use repeated addition, not only helps children use mental math to add and subtract, but also introduces them to equal groups and multiplication. As children expand their problem-solving skills and strategies, their fluency in single-digit sums and differences becomes routine.

The *Personal Math Trainer*'s standards quizzes allow for targeted practice to help build fluency. Use *Personal Math Trainer*: Standards Quiz 2.OA.B.2 to strengthen children's mastery of addition and subtraction within 20.

Continue concepts and skills practice with Lesson Check. Use Spiral Review to engage children in previously taught concepts and to promote content retention. Common Core standards are correlated to each section.

Lesson 3.11 228

Chapter 3
Review/Test

Summative Assessment

Use the **Chapter Review/Test** to assess children's progress in Chapter 3.

You may want to review with children the essential question for the chapter.

Chapter Essential Question

How can you use patterns and strategies to find sums and differences for basic facts?

Ask the following questions to focus children's thinking:

- **What are some strategies for remembering addition and subtraction facts?**
- **How are addition and subtraction related?**

Name _____

✓ **Chapter 3 Review/Test**

Personal Math Trainer
Online Assessment and Intervention

1. Erin puts 3 small cans, 4 medium cans, and 5 large cans on a shelf. How many cans does she put on the shelf?

   ___12___ cans

2. Fill in the bubble next to all the doubles facts you could use to find the sum of 3 + 2?

   ● 2 + 2
   ○ 5 + 5
   ● 3 + 3
   ○ 1 + 1

3. Does the number sentence have the same difference as 14 − 6 = ▧? Choose Yes or No.

10 − 1 = ▧	○ Yes	● No
10 − 2 = ▧	● Yes	○ No
10 − 3 = ▧	○ Yes	● No
10 − 4 = ▧	○ Yes	● No

Chapter 3

GO DIGITAL Assessment Options Chapter Test

two hundred twenty-nine **229**

---

4. Mr. Brown sold 5 red backpacks and 8 blue backpacks. Write the number sentence. Show how you can make a ten to find the sum. Write the sum.

   5 + 8 = ___13___
        ⟋ ⟍
        3 2
   10 + ___3___ = ___13___

5. Find the number of shapes in each row.

   □ □ □
   □ □ □
   □ □ □

   3 rows of ___4___

   Complete the addition sentence to find the total.

   ___4___ + ___4___ + ___4___ = ___12___

6. Tanya and 2 friends put rocks on the table. Each person put 2 rocks on the table. Draw a picture to show the groups of rocks.

Check children's drawings

   How many rocks did they put on the table?

   ___6___ rocks

230 two hundred thirty

✓ Data-Driven Decision Making ▲ RtI Chapter 3

Based on the results of the Chapter Review/Test use the following resources to review skills.

Item	Lesson	Standard	Content Focus	Personal Math Trainer	Intervene with
1	3.4	2.OA.B.2	Add 3 addends.	2.OA.B.2	R—3.4
2	3.1	2.OA.B.2	Identify doubles facts.	2.OA.B.2	R—3.1
3	3.7	2.OA.B.2	Use a tens fact to subtract.	2.OA.B.2	R—3.7
4	3.3	2.OA.B.2	Make a ten to find the sum.	2.OA.B.2	R—3.3
5	3.11	2.OA.C.4	Find number of objects in an array using repeated addition.	2.OA.C.4	R—3.11
6	3.10	2.OA.C.4	Represent number of objects in equal groups.	2.OA.C.4	R—3.10
7	3.5	2.OA.B.2	Represent subtraction problem using a drawing and a number sentence.	2.OA.B.2	R—3.5
8	3.5	2.OA.B.2	Represent problem using a drawing and a number sentence.	2.OA.B.2	R—3.5
9	3.2	2.OA.B.2	Represent addition problem using a number sentence.	2.OA.B.2	R—3.2
10	3.6	2.OA.B.2	Practice correct subtraction facts.	2.OA.B.2	R—3.6
11	3.10	2.OA.C.4	Solve problem involving equal groups.	2.OA.C.4	R—3.10
12	3.9	2.OA.A.1	Represent subtraction problem using a number sentence.	2.OA.A.1	R—3.9

Key: R—Reteach (in the *Chapter Resources*)

Personal Math Trainer

7. **THINK SMARTER+** Lily sees 15 tan puppies and 8 white puppies at the pet store. How many more tan puppies than white puppies does she see? Draw a picture and write a number sentence to solve.

Check children's drawings

$15 - 8 = 7$

_7_ more tan puppies

8. Mark counts 6 ducks in a pond and some ducks on the grass. There are 14 ducks in all. Draw a picture to show the two groups of ducks.

Check children's work. Drawings should show a group of 6 and a group of 8.

Write a number sentence that can help you find how many ducks are on the grass. Some possible answers are given.

_6_ + _8_ = _14_

How many ducks are on the grass? _8_ ducks

9. There are 8 peaches in a basket. Mrs. Dalton puts 7 more peaches in the basket. Complete the addition sentence to find how many peaches are in the basket now.

_8_ + _7_ = _15_   Also accept 7 + 8 = 15.

_15_ peaches

10. **GO DEEPER** Use the numbers on the tiles to write the differences. Then write the next fact in the pattern.

| 4 | 5 | 6 | 7 |

$12 - 6 =$ _6_ $11 - 6 =$ _5_

$12 - 7 =$ _5_ $12 - 6 =$ _6_

$12 - 8 =$ _4_ $13 - 6 =$ _7_

$12 - 9 = 3$ $14 - 6 = 8$

11. Jose wanted to share 18 strawberries with his brother equally. Draw a picture to show how Jose can share the strawberries.

Check children's work for understanding. There should be 2 rows of 9 strawberries.

How many strawberries will Jose receive?

_9_ strawberries

12. Hank has 13 grapes. He gives 5 grapes to his sister. How many grapes does Hank have now? Write a number sentence for the problem. Use ▓ for the missing number. Then solve.

$13 - 5 =$ ▓

_8_ grapes

Performance Assessment Tasks
Chapter 3

See the *Chapter Resources* for a Performance Task that assesses children's understanding of the content of this chapter.

For each task, you will find sample student work for each of the response levels in the task scoring rubric.

 Be sure to assign children Exercise 7 in the Personal Math Trainer. It features an animation or video to help children model and solve the problem.

Portfolio Performance Assessment Tasks may be used for portfolios.

Chapter 3 Review/Test

Summative Assessment

Use the **Chapter Test** to assess children's progress in Chapter 3.

Chapter Tests are provided in Common Core assessment formats in the *Chapter Resources*.

Personal Math Trainer

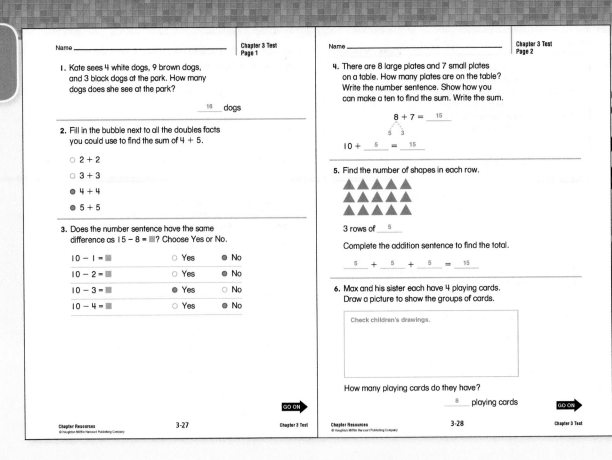

Chapter 3 Test — Page 1

1. Kate sees 4 white dogs, 9 brown dogs, and 3 black dogs at the park. How many dogs does she see at the park?

   16 dogs

2. Fill in the bubble next to all the doubles facts you could use to find the sum of 4 + 5.
   - ○ 2 + 2
   - ○ 3 + 3
   - ● 4 + 4
   - ● 5 + 5

3. Does the number sentence have the same difference as 15 − 8 = ■? Choose Yes or No.

10 − 1 = ■	○ Yes	● No
10 − 2 = ■	○ Yes	● No
10 − 3 = ■	● Yes	○ No
10 − 4 = ■	○ Yes	● No

Chapter 3 Test — Page 2

4. There are 8 large plates and 7 small plates on a table. How many plates are on the table? Write the number sentence. Show how you can make a ten to find the sum. Write the sum.

   8 + 7 = 15
   5 3
   10 + 5 = 15

5. Find the number of shapes in each row.

   3 rows of 5

   Complete the addition sentence to find the total.

   5 + 5 + 5 = 15

6. Max and his sister each have 4 playing cards. Draw a picture to show the groups of cards.

   Check children's drawings.

   How many playing cards do they have?

   8 playing cards

✓ Data-Driven Decision Making — RtI

Based on the results of the Chapter Test use the following resources to review skills.

Item	Lesson	Standard	Content Focus	Personal Math Trainer	Intervene with
1	3.4	2.OA.B.2	Add 3 addends.	2.OA.B.2	R—3.4
2	3.1	2.OA.B.2	Identify doubles facts.	2.OA.B.2	R—3.1
3	3.7	2.OA.B.2	Use a tens fact to subtract.	2.OA.B.2	R—3.7
4	3.3	2.OA.B.2	Make a ten to find the sum.	2.OA.B.2	R—3.3
5	3.11	2.OA.C.4	Find the number of objects in an array using repeated addition.	2.OA.C.4	R—3.11
6, 11	3.10	2.OA.C.4	Represent and solve problems involving equal groups.	2.OA.C.4	R—3.10
7, 8	3.5	2.OA.B.2	Use related addition and subtraction facts.	2.OA.B.2	R—3.5
9	3.2	2.OA.B.2	Practice addition facts.	2.OA.B.2	R—3.2
10	3.6	2.OA.B.2	Practice subtraction facts.	2.OA.B.2	R—3.6
12	3.9	2.OA.A.1	Represent subtraction problem using a number sentence.	2.OA.A.1	R—3.9

Key: **R**—Reteach (in the *Chapter Resources*)

7. Ling sees 13 birds in a tree
and 5 birds on the ground.
How many more birds does Ling
see in the tree than on the ground?
Draw a picture and write a number
sentence to solve.

Check children's drawings.

$13 - 5 = 8$

___8___ more birds

8. Sarah uses 4 markers to color her picture.
She has 11 markers in all. Draw a picture
to show the two groups of markers.

Check children's work. Drawings should show a
group of 4 and a group of 7.

Write a number sentence that can help you
find how many markers Sarah does not use.
Possible answer is given.

___4___ + ___7___ = ___11___

How many markers does Sarah not use?

___7___ markers

9. There are 9 oranges in a bag. Mr. Johnson puts 4 more
oranges in the bag. Complete the addition sentence
to find how many oranges are in the bag now.

___9___ + ___4___ = ___13___

___13___ oranges

GO ON ▶

10. Use the numbers on the tiles to write the differences.
Then write the next fact in the pattern.

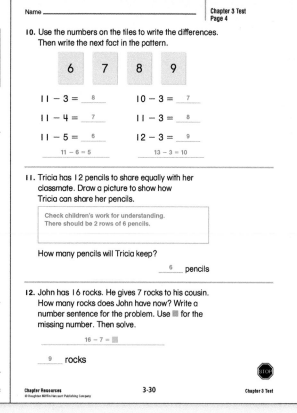

| 6 | 7 | 8 | 9 |

$11 - 3 = $ ___8___ $10 - 3 = $ ___7___

$11 - 4 = $ ___7___ $11 - 3 = $ ___8___

$11 - 5 = $ ___6___ $12 - 3 = $ ___9___

___$11 - 6 = 5$___   ___$13 - 3 = 10$___

11. Tricia has 12 pencils to share equally with her
classmate. Draw a picture to show how
Tricia can share her pencils.

Check children's work for understanding.
There should be 2 rows of 6 pencils.

How many pencils will Tricia keep?

___6___ pencils

12. John has 16 rocks. He gives 7 rocks to his cousin.
How many rocks does John have now? Write a
number sentence for the problem. Use ■ for the
missing number. Then solve.

___$16 - 7 = $ ■___

___9___ rocks

STOP

Portfolio Suggestions
The portfolio represents the
growth, talents, achievements,
and reflections of the
mathematics learner. Children
might spend a short time
selecting work samples
for their portfolios.

You may want to have
children respond to the
following questions:

• **How do you think you did
on this test?**

• **What do you understand
about the chapter that you
did not understand before
the chapter?**

• **What would you like to
learn more about?**

For information about how to
organize, share, and evaluate
portfolios, see the *Chapter
Resources.*

Chapter 3 Test   232B